Anthony Reuben was the BBC's first head of statistics and now works on the corporation's fact-checking Reality Check brand, which he created. Anthony has 23 years' experience in journalism, and has been read by millions of readers of the BBC News website over the past 12 years. He has twice won the Royal Statistical Society's award for excellence in journalism and been shortlisted twice for the British Journalism Awards.

STATISTICAL

*Ten Easy Ways to Avoid
Being Misled By Numbers*

Anthony Reuben

CONSTABLE

CONSTABLE

First published in Great Britain in 2019 by Constable

1 3 5 7 9 10 8 6 4 2

A CIP catalogue record for this book
is available from the British Library.

ISBN: 978-1-47213-026-6

Typeset in Stone Serif by Hewer Text UK Ltd, Edinburgh
Printed and bound in Great Britain by Clays Ltd, Elcograf S.p.A.

Papers used by Constable are from well-managed
forests and other responsible sources.

Constable
An imprint of
Little, Brown Book Group
Carmelite House
50 Victoria Embankment
London EC4Y 0DZ

An Hachette UK Company
www.hachette.co.uk

www.littlebrown.co.uk

For Susan, Isaac, Emily and Boaz

Contents

Contents

The most powerful question

There's no getting away from statistics, however hard you try. Open a newspaper and see how long it takes you to find the first item based on numbers. It might be a poll about what people think of the US president or the latest figures showing what has happened to wages. Perhaps the country is experiencing record temperatures or the head of the NHS is arguing that the organisation needs more money. We use them every day.

It's not just in the news either. The company you work for may be revealing its gender pay gap or your child's school could be contacting you about its funding for the year. Your friends could be arguing about who is the greatest English batsman of all time or whether they should buy a petrol or diesel car. Perhaps you are trying to choose between different loans or just deciding whether to take an umbrella out with you today.

There are numbers everywhere you look and not all of them should be believed. That figure you have just seen on social media is very enticing – it feels like a proper fact and it supports your case in an argument you've been having with your friends. You've seen a claim that pay growth is at its worst level since the Napoleonic wars – is that true, and is it a fair comparison? Before you share a statistic, you really need to challenge it and look a bit further into where it comes from.

Unfortunately, lots of people do not have the confidence to challenge the numbers they read. Do you? Journalists, even some very good ones, get nervous around statistics and will not investigate them the way they would any other sort of evidence. Politicians, academics, people from all walks of life aren't comfortable with interpreting and under-standing the way numbers are presented to them. You find researchers at their wits' end trying to prepare briefings for ministers or presenters to get statistical arguments across in a way that will be absorbed. We can be very critical when presented with an argument, but people who confidently question what they hear on the radio, or read in a newspaper, will happily accept the figures in a news story without challenging them, and move on. Normally cynical people will read the results of a survey and click the share button without a second thought about whether it is robust.

This is partly because it is considered acceptable to be hopeless with numbers in a way that it isn't with words. I have lost count of the number of times colleagues and friends have told me they can't cope with figures, but I very rarely hear anybody admit to being unable to spell or construct a sentence. We classify certain jobs as ones for the numerate (accountants, rocket scientists, actuaries) and decide that people in other jobs do not need to be able to cope with numbers at all.

In my experience, the mistakes made with numbers are usually made not in the numbers themselves but in the words used to describe them. And that's good news for you, because it means it's much easier to correct yourself – people tend to be much more comfortable with words than they are with numbers.

But a lack of confidence with numbers is a problem because there are many questionable ones out there and it's easy to be misled. Some of them are deliberately there to mislead you and artificially strengthen an argument; some of them are misleading by accident, because the person presenting them did not have the confidence or knowledge to check; and some are just thrown in to make a story sound more authoritative.

Without an understanding of data it's very hard to follow what's going on in your country. If you don't have at least a rough idea of what the population is or how many people are unemployed or how many people migrate to or leave the country each year, lots of political arguments become meaningless. If you have ever watched Prime Minister's Questions and wondered why the prime minister is claiming that crime is falling while the leader of the opposition claims that crime is rising, you'll be completely bemused unless you know that there are two completely different sets of crime statistics, one based on a survey and one based on crimes recorded by the police. When the leader of the opposition says that a public service is desperately short of cash and the prime minister says it is receiving record funding, you need to know that record funding is the norm, otherwise services struggle to cope with a growing population and inflation.

Statistics don't need to be scary. If you can add, subtract, multiply and divide then you already have most of the tools you need to challenge the numbers all around you. And in this book you'll find the other tools you need to deal with the things you hear that set off alarm bells in your head.

Take, for example, a 2018 report about plastic consumption in the UK. Following lots of justified concern about plastic waste, sparked by David Attenborough's *Blue Planet II* towards the end of 2017, the government launched a consultation about whether it should ban single-use plastic straws. There was research that demonstrated that we use 42 billion single-use plastic straws per year in the UK. There was all sorts of interesting background material about market research and dividing EU figures by levels of economic output for each country; the statistics would take ages to reproduce if you wanted to check them and it would be a pretty daunting thing to do. Still, we know that loads of straws get used in the UK, and this is certainly a big number, so why not just share it?

Here's why: if you just divide the number of straws by the population of the UK (just over 65 million) it turns out the report is suggesting that people in the UK consume an average of about 650 plastic straws each per year – that's almost two a day. My children were pretty enthusiastic consumers of plastic straws before we invested in a set of reusable silicone ones, but even they would have struggled to get through 650 each a year. That's not to say that the policy was wrong or we shouldn't be concerned about single-use plastics. The questionable stats were a distraction from the environmental message.

Without trying to dismantle the methodology behind the claim we have come to a pretty robust conclusion about whether we should believe it. And that is what this book is about.

This book will teach you in ten chapters how to get to the simple questions such as how many straws is it per person, which will allow you to challenge figures painlessly. The key to it is that before tackling data there is one question we should ask every time we are suspicious about the numbers. This is the greatest gift that I am giving to every reader of this book, even those who are just skimming through the introduction while standing around in a bookshop: it's the most powerful question in journalism.

It's not a question that you ask politicians or chief executives such as 'Are you going to resign?' That's sometimes a good question, but it's not as powerful as this question that you should ask yourself every time you watch, hear or read a news story.

So here it is – fanfare please.

Is this reasonably likely to be true?

This was a question I was taught by my father – a scientist – to use when checking my homework. You don't need to go back and carry out the calculation again. It's enough to look at the original question and estimate approximately what you think the answer should be so you can see if your own solution looks to be in the right ballpark.

This is the great insight when you're trying to challenge numbers. Many people are scared of numbers because they think it's their job to be right to three decimal places. Unless you're the person doing the original research and coming up with the figures, that's not true. When you're trying to decide whether to believe something or look into it further, you need to know that it's approximately in the right area.

What makes the most powerful question so useful is that the sort of figures you can use to work out if something is reasonably likely to be true do not have to be anything like as copper-bottomed as the numbers you would have to use if you were doing the research yourself. You can use any old thing you find on the internet, you can use stuff that folk have told you in the pub or vague ideas you have in your head. The idea is just to find out whether a figure seems suspicious and whether you should be looking further into it or seeking help from an expert.

Take the notorious *Daily Telegraph* headline in June 2010: 'Public pensions cost you £4,000 a year'. The story was that the cost of paying public sector pensions was going to rise over the next five years to £4000 a year per household in the UK.

How would you set about finding out whether that was reasonably likely to be true? If you wanted to find out whether it was precisely true then you would have to find out the total cost of public sector pensions and divide it by the number of house-holds, but if you know both of those figures off the top of your head then you probably don't need to be reading this book.

A better approach would be to think about what would be a reasonable estimate of how much the average household earns in a year. You could even think about what your own household earns, unless

you consider yourself to be fabulously rich or unrepresentatively poor.

There are various figures used for this but if you're
using anything around about £27,000 then you're
on the right track.

Now consider how much tax you are paying on
that. You could work that out precisely, but on this
sort of income, taking into account the amount
you're allowed to earn without paying tax, income
tax and national insurance together will come to
around about 20 per cent. But it doesn't matter if
you have guessed a bit more than that or a bit less.
The point is that the figure you end up with is not
going to be dramatically more than £4000 in tax. So
if that much from each household is to be spent on
public sector pensions, you need to ask who is going
to pay for the NHS or schools or any of the other
services that the government needs to fund.

The clear conclusion is that this figure is not
reasonably likely to be true. And indeed, later in the
day the *Telegraph* change the headline on its website
to 'Public pensions to cost you £400 a year'.

With only a little bit of elementary maths – dividing stuff by other stuff and using percentages – you
can easily work out if something is close to
accurate.

There will be hardly any sums to do and no unreasonably tricky mathematical concepts. As long as
you hear the alarm bells at the right time you can

treat stories with due suspicion, and go and seek expert help if necessary. No longer will you need to be scared by stories about the growing risk of things or threats that will bankrupt the economy. Armed with the most powerful question, you will be free to go about your life without being misled by dubious statistics and bogus claims.

I stepped out of the front door the other morning and it was raining. I was about to pop back inside and put on a raincoat but then I looked at the weather app on my phone and it said there was a 0 per cent chance of rain. So I walked through the park in the rain and got wet. If only I had had the confidence to ask the most powerful question, I could have stayed dry.

It's not just about avoiding being misled or getting wet. You will also find joy in having the confidence to challenge statistics from colleagues and friends. In a competitive job market, if you're the one who questions whether the figures in a report sound likely, you will be on the way to the top. I describe myself as being a numerical pedant – now you can be the numerical pedant in your crowd. It's great fun and very satisfying.

I too find myself trying to cope in groups with massively more numerical expertise than I have. When I was the BBC's head of statistics I was invited to a one-day conference in Oxford to discuss whether there should be a global statistics authority. When I arrived there were 20 people around the table and it turned out I was the only one who wasn't the head of a national statistics office or didn't have a professorship, a knighthood or a Nobel Prize. I was probably just there to make up the numbers, although that is generally frowned upon in such circles. When it was time to go round the table for everyone to introduce themselves I noticed that the more important a person was, the fewer words they needed to use. Everybody there knew who 'Joe from Columbia' was (it was Joseph Stiglitz, the Nobel Prize-winning economist). I introduced myself as 'Anthony from the BBC' and added 'I'm here representing all the users.'

I've written this book for all the users as well, especially the involuntary ones. We are all users of statistics whether we like it or not, and everyone needs the confidence to challenge the numbers they hear. I am here to tell you that you already have most of the skills you need to question the numbers you see every day.

CHAPTER 1

Surveys

Guilty until proven innocent

You will never open a newspaper without finding at least one story based on a survey. I never open my email without finding one. They claim to tell me what UK workers think, or what business leaders think, or which animals are most popular in particular countries. Let me say up front: I believe that surveys must be considered guilty until proven innocent because some of the most dubious statistics you will ever see come from them. But there is a huge range of credibility for surveys. Some of them are unbelievably spurious, based on about seven people's views of a subject they are unlikely to be honest about. Others are the best-available figures, providing insight into difficult subjects.

One of the highest-profile official statistics in the UK is the monthly unemployment figures and they're based on a huge survey. The Bureau of Labor

Statistics in the USA conducts an even bigger survey. It's important to be able to spot which surveys you can believe and which you should reject. Whether people believe huge, sweeping statements about what the population thinks really matters.

My favourite dubious survey of all time started with the claim that 'a Saturday night in costs hosts up to £118.29 on average'. Notice how the writer has combined 'up to' with 'on average' to give a completely meaningless figure. Also notice the oddly specific figure, which I assure you is not justified by what is to come.

The figure is based on the idea that people (mainly women apparently) are inviting four guests over to watch *Strictly Come Dancing* or *The X Factor* and buying refreshments for them. The spending per person is £11.24 on alcohol, £10.92 on takeaways, £6.23 on snacks (that's a lot of chips and dips) and £6.32 on soft drinks. That spending on soft drinks looks particularly high – I reckon you should be able to get about eight litres of fizzy drinks for that, enough to quench even the strongest thirst, especially when you have already consumed at least eight cans of beer or a bottle or two of wine. But it's the cost of a takeaway that I love the most because the press release includes the methodology behind this one. It's based on 'desk research' that has involved finding out how much set menus for four cost at Chinese restaurants in Cardiff, London and Manchester, and Indian restaurants in Fife, Nottingham and Bournemouth.

But I've saved the best aspect of the research until last, which is that their survey has established that 55 per cent of women bought a new outfit to wear in front of the television, 'inspired by the glamorous judges on *X Factor* and outlandish outfits on *Strictly* – spending up to £100'. It's a triumphantly terrible piece of work.

Later in the chapter, I'm going to take you through some more of my favourite dubious surveys and in the next chapter I'm going to look at opinion polls around elections. First, I'm going to run through how you can tell when surveys aren't as robust as they might be.

Imagine you're trying to find out what people in your country think about cats. How would you go about finding out? The most accurate way would be to ask everybody in the country what they thought about cats. You need to get your questions about cats to millions of people and make sure they answer. That's how censuses work. Every ten years a questionnaire gets sent out to every household and they are legally required to complete it. So you could put a question about cats on the census. The trouble is, the census is an expensive project and it takes ages, so you won't get to find out what people think of cats for years. And you need to know this week, for some urgent, cat-related reason.

That's why people conduct surveys. The idea is that if you can get a smaller group that has the same features as the whole population, you can just ask the smaller group and then say that's what everyone in the country thinks. Doing that properly is jolly difficult, but people try to do it all the time. If you see the results of a survey and are worried you are being misled, there are five questions to ask:

- Where has the survey come from?

- What questions does the survey ask?

- How many people were asked?

- Were they the right people to ask?

- Is the organisation making reasonable claims based on the results?

Where has the survey come from?

There are two parts to this question: who conducted the research and who paid them to do it?

The answers to these questions should not disqualify the survey immediately, but they will put you on your guard and make you look more carefully at the answers to the other questions. It helps if the organisation conducting the survey is a member of a body such as the British Polling Council because it means that the way it conducted the research should be easier to find, but it does not mean the research is necessarily reliable. Also, there are large research organisations that do some sensible work that are not members of such a body so it's not a definitive guide, but it is a useful shortcut.

You should be more suspicious if the organisation that has paid for the research has an obvious interest in the outcome, so if the report saying that everyone loves cats comes from a manufacturer of kitty litter then it should put you on your guard, but it doesn't necessarily mean that the conclusions are nonsense.

I received a press release saying that 30 per cent of people would consider taking a holiday at a site affected by radiation. It was sent by a company that makes equipment that protects you from radiation. The figure might still have been true, and it may indeed be the case that holidays in Chernobyl are flying off the shelves. On the other hand, there were no details given of how they reached that figure of 30 per cent or indeed who had conducted the research. Do you want the news you hear to be influenced by this company? This is really one to avoid.

Another important thing to be aware of is that the organisation that conducted the research may just be using data from its own customers. So, for example, a health insurance company may be using the answers it has been given by its members when they sign up. This is a problem because it is extremely unlikely that they will be representative of the whole of the country – they're likely to be unrepresentatively wealthy for starters. I'll return to this when I talk about which people are asked later in the chapter, but beware research coming from organisations with access to lots of their own data.

What questions does the survey ask?

See if you can find what questions were being asked in the survey – if it's a reputable pollster they should be easy to find. If someone stopped you in the street and asked you those questions, would you be sure what they meant or are they ambiguous? Do you feel they might be trying to point you towards a particular answer? If you were asked, 'Do you just adore lovely, fluffy, beautiful, cute little kittens?' you might be more likely to respond with positive feline sentiments than if you were just asked, 'What do you think about cats?'

There was a scene in the classic BBC sitcom *Yes, Prime Minister* when the wizened permanent secretary Sir Humphrey asked young, inexperienced assistant Bernard a series of questions about whether he felt young people needed discipline and direction in their lives, leading up to the question of whether national service should be reintroduced. He then asked a series of questions about whether young people should be forced to take up arms against their will or given weapons and taught how to kill, leading up to the same question about conscription. It meant that Bernard agreed both that national service should and shouldn't be reintroduced, which Sir Humphrey described as 'the perfect balanced sample'.

Bernard was led by the earlier questions towards giving opposite answers to the final question. It's usually pretty obvious if a pollster is trying to lead respondents in a particular direction when you look at the questions asked.

Here's a real-life example: before the publication in 2012 of the Leveson Inquiry report into press standards in the UK, the polling organisation YouGov was commissioned to conduct different surveys by the *Sun* and the Media Standards Trust (MST). In the MST survey, 79 per cent of respondents agreed that 'there should be an independent body established by law, which deals with complaints and decides what sanctions there should be if journalists break agreed codes of conduct'. That seems to be at odds with the survey conducted on behalf of the *Sun*, in which only 24 per cent of respondents thought that the best way to regulate the press would be through 'a regulatory body set up through law by Parliament, with rules agreed by MPs'. This was the same polling organisation conducting surveys for different customers and getting fundamentally different answers to the same question. Except it wasn't quite the same question. YouGov's Peter Kellner explained that the difference lay in the way the question was framed, in particular the fact that the first question asked about an independent body established by law, while the second said it would be set up through law by Parliament, with rules agreed by MPs. While these two proposals are fundamentally the same thing, it turns out we don't like to think of MPs being involved with press regulation, so when they were mentioned it made respondents uneasy.

Another example is a survey that asked whether people were saving money in a pension to help pay for social care in retirement. Imagine how you would answer that question. You may be saving money in a pension, but might not have been thinking about social care when you started saving. Some people would have said 'yes' because they were saving, and so that money could help to fund their social care if they needed it. Others would say 'no' because they were not specifically saving to fund their social care. The question was not clear enough, so the results of the survey were completely unreliable.

Polling guru David Cowling sent me another example from the height of the financial crisis in October 2008, when the pollsters ComRes conducted two surveys of about 1000 people, asking what they thought about bailouts. One for the *Independent on Sunday* asked: 'Is it right that taxpayers' money should be used to bail out the banks?': 37 per cent said yes, 58 per cent said no and 5 per cent didn't know. In a survey the same month for the BBC's *Daily Politics*, the same pollsters asked whether people agreed with the statement: 'I support the government using taxpayers' money to stabilise the financial system': 50 per cent did, 41 per cent didn't and 9 per cent didn't know. Two polls in the same month conducted by the same organisation received very different answers to the same question. Presumably the difference was because one of them mentioned bailing out banks, which people were generally unenthusiastic about, while the other talked about stabilising the financial system, which respondents thought was a good idea.

You should also consider whether you think people are likely to answer the questions honestly. I was sent a survey of whether people smacked their children. I was assured that it was anonymised, but given that it is socially unacceptable to smack children, it means people are very unlikely to admit to it, even in an anonymous poll. Separately, I saw a survey of 16- to 18-year-olds, most of whom claimed that getting good qualifications was their top priority, they weren't very interested in sex and what they really liked was spending time with their families. I wonder if they thought they might be overheard by their parents.

The same problem with the likelihood of getting accurate responses is true when you conduct a survey of whether people have broken the law – the results will be unreliable.

How many people were asked?

If you're going to say something about a large number of people, it's no good just asking one or two of them. You would be amazed at the amount of press releases I see in which they have asked a few hundred people and are trying to use that to make claims about a whole country. Kellogg's based the claim that its new recipe for Coco Pops was loved by kids on asking 100 of them. And the claim that it was approved of by mums was based on asking 200 of them. The general rule is: if you're trying to say something about a population of 20,000 people or more, you need to have responses from at least 1000. Some of the smallest sample sizes you will see are on adverts for cosmetics, in which, for example, a company may say that 80 per cent of women agree that a particular lip gloss makes their lips look visibly plumper, and it's based on asking 43 women. I'm assured by the Advertising Standards Authority (ASA) that if the claim was about something more important such as whether a particular product will stop your baby having tummy ache, it would take more notice and demand proper evidence. The ASA doesn't care as much about how visibly plump your lips are. It's possible that a company could get away with making claims about lip plumpness without asking any women at all.

If you're trying to say something about a population smaller than 20,000, getting a representative sample becomes more difficult. If you want to know whether professional football managers like cats, for example, you would really have to ask all of them. That's because there are so few professional managers that the margin of error if you just asked a few of them would be enormous. Consider an extreme example – you are the conductor of a choir with ten members and you want to decide what combination of show tunes and Christmas carols to perform at your next concert. If you're going to base it on which is preferred by members of the choir, you couldn't get a reliable estimate of that by asking just half of your singers because there's no reason to believe that half would be representative – it may be that the other five would completely disagree. The only solution would be to ask everyone.

But there's another way round the problem of saying something about a small population. Everyone understands that it's difficult to get answers from all professional football managers, so they're not going to think any less of you if you have only got answers from half of them. 'We spoke to half of all professional football managers and found that most of them think cats are great,' is a perfectly reasonable, if slightly random, newsline. What you can't do with that data is claim that the majority of football managers think cats are great.

I used to get sent a regular survey of what chief financial officers (CFOs) from UK companies think. The company that calculated it spoke to about 100 CFOs every three months and sent out the results. That's fine – CFOs are not particularly easy people to survey, so if they had started with 'a survey of about 100 CFOs has found . . .' people would have understood what they were getting and that it might not be strictly representative. But, in fact, they always sent round press releases claiming to show what UK CFOs think as a whole. Talking to 100 of them isn't good enough to do that, even if you have the CFOs of a number of major companies, when there are many thousands of companies in the UK that could have a CFO. Compare that with the Ifo survey of business confidence in Germany, which hears from 7000 companies a month. Or the Tankan survey in Japan, which speaks to more than 10,000 companies a month.

You also need to beware surveys that have broken down their results further than the sample size will allow. For example, I was sent the results of a survey of

2000 people from five European countries, asking whether they ever pretended to be ill to get a day off work. First of all, this survey suffers from the same problems as the smacking one – would you be likely to admit to it? But 2000 is a perfectly reasonable sample size to say something general about the five European countries, or even to break it down into whether men or women are more likely to feign illness. What it couldn't do was then look at the skiving habits of French workers (who it claimed were the most likely to pretend to be ill) because it would only have spoken to about 400 of them. We'll return to the problems of unwarranted sick-day statistics in Chapter 8.

As the size of the population you're talking about increases, that 1000 minimum number of responses stays the same, but the next question gets harder.

Were they the right people to ask?

Speaking to the right people is remarkably difficult and if you haven't spoken to the right ones it doesn't matter how many people have been surveyed. Even if you interview a million readers of *Cats Monthly*, it's not going to tell you anything about what people in general (who do not, on the whole, subscribe to cat publications) think about cats.

Remember, you're trying to get a representative sample, so you need the relatively small group of people to whom you're talking to have the same qualities as the whole population about whom you're trying to say something. How do you go about doing that? If you stand on a busy high street and ask passers-by, the answers you get are going to be skewed towards people who live in the area, who might be richer than the country as a whole, or older, or more likely to be allergic to cats. And they will certainly be the ones with unrepresentatively large amounts of time on their hands because they have stopped and answered your questions.

There are two potential solutions to this problem and they each have their shortcomings.

The classic way of dealing with this is to get a completely random sample of people from within your population. A popular way of doing this is to get the phone book, randomly choose numbers from it and keep phoning them until enough people have responded, generally 1000. Nowadays, this skews the results towards older people who are more likely to have landlines and to answer them.

After the 2015 general election in the UK, Martin Boon from the pollsters ICM revealed that in order to get 2000 responses they were having to call about 30,000 random numbers, which raises the great danger that the people prepared to answer both the phone and the questions are not representative. When such a small proportion of people are answering the questions, you have to wonder if there is something unusual about them – perhaps they are older than the population as a whole or unrepresentatively interested in politics.

Many polling companies have started using mobile phone numbers as well, but only a relatively small proportion compared with landlines. The best practice way of getting a random sample is what the Office for National Statistics does with the Labour Force Survey, which is to choose households at random and then send people round to knock on doors, returning if nobody is at home. Once initial contact has been made, further interviews may be conducted over the phone. That's an expensive way of finding a sample, and most organisation's commissioning polls can't afford it.

The other way of getting what you hope will be a representative sample is to build up a panel of people who you know lots about. Then, if a client comes to you and says they want to do some research into what Belgian women who work full-time and like ice cream think about something, you can get in touch with them straight away, while making sure that the group you have is representative in other ways such as age and geographical spread across Belgium. You have to pay people a small amount to be on these panels, and the online access means it will be skewed towards younger people with internet access. There have been suggestions that the system provides incentives for people to lie about their characteristics to make themselves likely to be polled more often. And this gets to the nub of the problem – the people on your panel will be unrepresentatively interested in completing surveys. Also, it's unclear where you stop in identifying features that make the sample representative – age, gender, race, income, class, location, employment status, marital status – you could go on forever.

In either the random method or the panel method, the pollsters may make adjustments to their findings so that they become more representative. If you don't have quite enough older people in your sample, for example, you might give the answers that you did get from older people greater weight. The problem with this is that there is a danger that the pollster will start adjusting the results towards what they are expecting to happen, as we'll discuss in the next chapter on political polling.

Is the organisation making reasonable claims based on the results?

If the results of a survey claim to show that the world is massively different to how you thought, it is almost certainly because there is a mistake in the survey.

Even the biggest surveys are imprecise and have margins of error, which will be discussed in Chapter 9.

That needs to be reflected in the language used. Surveys do not 'show' or 'prove' anything, they 'suggest' things.

Looking deeply into the methodology may sound like a lot of effort to go to when you're just trying to find out if an alluring figure you heard on the news is reasonably likely to be true. So for those of you who don't have the time, there are a few quick things you can do to check.

A good start is to think about whether it's likely the people who conducted the survey would have been able to find out what they claim to have discovered. Is it something people are likely to be happy talking about? Now, check if it's easy to find out how the survey was conducted. And look at whether they seem to have gone to any trouble to make sure their sample is genuinely representative. Now, try explaining in a sentence what they have done to get these figures. If you can say it out loud without feeling ridiculous, that's a good sign.

The biggest thing to look out for is self-selecting samples. It's very tempting when you have lots of customers visiting your website, or lots of people reading your magazine or lots of followers on Twitter, to ask them what they think and publish the results. As long as you show your workings, that's fine. You might be interested in which player visitors to the Boston Red Sox website think was the best last month, but the editors presumably would not suggest that was representative of what the whole country thought. When a police force conducted a survey among its followers on Twitter, asking what they thought of spit hoods, who did they think it was representative of? It turned out that 93 per cent of the 1300 people who voted thought that the devices that were meant to prevent suspects spitting or biting were a good thing (and this was widely reported) but are followers of the police force's Twitter account likely to be a microcosm of the population as a whole? I suggest not.

To sum up the five questions, let's consider the questions you would ask about a recent finding that 56 per cent of three- and four-year-olds own their own connected device such as a tablet, PC or mobile phone. The figure just for tablets is 47 per cent. Instinctively, this feels high, especially because similar research the previous year from the regulator Ofcom found that 21 per cent of that age group owned a tablet. So let's look a bit further.

1. Where has the survey come from?
   It comes from a market research organisation that sells reports giving insights into children and young people. In this case, it's part of a big report into the use of media by children. They appear to have conducted the research themselves and there is no obvious reason for them to be biased either way.

2. What questions does the survey ask?

   The question asked was, 'Does your child have their own personal device from the following?' and then there was a list of devices. So no ambiguity there.

3. How many people were asked?

   The survey was completed by 500 parents of three- and four-year-olds. Where parents had more than one child in the correct age group the software was clear regarding which child they were supposed to be answering the questions about. The sample size is a bit small, but not small enough to explain the difference between 47 per cent and 21 per cent having tablets. Ofcom's survey was done by 600 parents.

4. Were they the right people to ask?

   Parents were found via one of the UK's largest online panels and they were chosen in order to have balance between mothers and fathers of boys and girls, and also across socio-economic groups. Ofcom, on the other hand, interviewed people face to face. It's possible that an online survey would capture more technophile parents or that some parents who could be embarrassed to admit to an interviewer that their three-year-old owned a tablet would be happy to say so online. But it's hard to imagine that either of these would have a huge effect.

5. Is the organisation making reasonable claims based on the results?

   It's tricky. Two sets of researchers have gone to considerable lengths to find the answer to a question and have reached very different figures. Neither method is perfect, but the flaws do not appear to explain the disparity. Sometimes you just get funny results from surveys, which is why you should never attach too much weight to their findings. It would probably be best not to refer to either figure on its own or to make very strong claims about either until you find a reason why they are so different.

Now you know about the five questions you need to ask to avoid being misled by surveys, you are ready to see what you are up against.

My favourite dubious surveys

I once suggested in a talk at the Royal Statistical Society that it should have a special section for people who make up numbers. I imagined that it would be like the marketing department in the company where the comic-strip character Dilbert works, where it's just one long party and every Friday they barbecue a unicorn (apparently that's a good thing). Are they having more fun than I am? I suspect their working lives must be the same as everybody else's – mostly humdrum with occasional days of excitement. The same may be said of the emails I receive from public relations companies every day. Most of them get deleted straight away, but every now and then there is a pure act of creativity that sets it apart from the usual nonsense and wins it a place in a special folder on my email system. It is some of the contents of that folder that I am now going to share with you. I will avoid mentioning the companies involved, either to avoid shaming the guilty parties, or because, despite their genius, I still don't want to promote their products.

Big number costings are a mainstay of press releases. Scrolling through my special folder I am told that people not having enough sleep is costing the economy £37 billion a year, which is coincidentally exactly the same amount as bad customer service is costing companies. Lack of neighbourliness costs the economy £14 billion a year, the skills shortage costs UK businesses £2.2 billion a year, people watching the Olympics when they're meant to be working will cost the UK economy £1.6 billion, financial crime costs the UK economy £52 billion even though hardly any of it is ever reported, having unhealthy employees is costing £57 billion, which is a touch more than the £56 billion a year they lose to poor training, and absenteeism costs the UK economy a nice big round £100 billion a year.

Looking further afield, muscle and joint pain cost European economies up to 240 billion euros a year, solar storms could cost the US economy $40 billion a day and the German national brand (whatever that is) was devalued by $191 million by the Volkswagen diesel scandal. While we're looking at the big numbers, it turns out that clumsy Brits lost £3.2 billion worth of wedding and engagement rings over the last five years.

There will be more about why costings in general are bogus in Chapter 3 and the dangers of meaningless big numbers in Chapter 6, but you can probably spot a few flaws with these ones even before you have read those chapters.

How about the research that found that 43 per cent of car accidents happen during rush hour, a figure described as 'almost half' in the press release? That doesn't seem particularly surprising, given that you would expect more accidents to happen when there were more cars on the road. But if you look in the footnotes, it turns out that they're counting rush hour as being weekdays from 6 a.m. to 10 a.m. and then 4 p.m. to 8 p.m., and suddenly it seems extraordinary that such a small proportion of accidents happen during those periods. The headline should be 'Staggeringly small number of accidents happen during rush hour'.

On the list of surveys that make me wonder how they got people to admit to things comes the survey from a recruitment company that found 37 per cent of people had admitted lying on their CVs. Be particularly careful when participants are being asked questions to which they are unlikely to give an honest answer. I was entertained by a press release that said: 'A third of people in the UK will not give truthful answers about themselves when asked questions by pollsters, according to a new survey.' In paradoxical terms, that is well up there with the words of Psalm 116: 'I said in my haste, "all men are liars".'

I love an obviously self-serving piece of research such as the survey from a company that makes technology for controlling office buildings that found 84 per cent of workers felt their productivity was seriously stunted by their inability to control the office temperature and 81 per cent would consider moving jobs for a more technologically advanced office.

A company that makes hearses reported that 91 per cent of people don't know what to do when encountering a funeral procession. But it was not a survey of the general public, it was a survey of funeral directors, 198 of them to be precise. And 91 per cent of them said people were either 'not fully aware' of what was expected of them or didn't know at all. That doesn't mean 91 per cent of people don't know what to do, it means 91 per cent of funeral directors think people don't know what to do. And maybe not even that, because it's a pretty small sample.

I must end with research that found that dogs watch around 214 hours of TV per year – equivalent to more than two years of *EastEnders* – with BBC One being the most-watched channel. Sometimes you wonder not just about the methodology, but about the point.

Avoiding being misled by surveys is all about training yourself so that alarm bells go off when you hear about them. I hope yours have been jangling throughout the last few pages.

Take as a starting point that surveys are guilty until proven innocent, then apply the five questions and you should be able to live your life untroubled by survey-induced nonsense.

CHAPTER 2

Opinion Polls

Should you believe them?

Let's take what you now know about surveys and apply it to political opinion polls. Around election times they generally ask which party people are planning to vote for. Which party is leading in the polls becomes a key part of the narrative around election campaigns, so there are even fresh polls straight after a televised debate to see which party has benefited the most from it. Polls can be interesting, but it's important not to accept them as gospel truth and it's especially important not to take too much notice of a single poll.

This is why: two weeks before the referendum on Scottish independence in 2014, the *Sunday Times* published a YouGov poll, which put the 'Yes' campaign ahead by 51 per cent to 49 per cent, excluding the 'don't knows'. Seemingly as a direct result of this, Chancellor George Osborne announced that a timetable would be set out for giving more powers to the Scottish Parliament if there was a 'No' vote, including more powers to raise taxes. The following day the news was knocked off the top spot by the announcement that the Duchess of Cambridge was expecting her second child, but former Prime Minister Gordon Brown set out the timetable for devolving more powers. The government in Westminster denied it was panicking but announced that instead of attending Prime Minister's Questions, Prime Minister David Cameron and Labour leader Ed Miliband would be heading to Scotland to campaign for a 'No' vote. Deputy Prime Minister Nick Clegg would also be travelling north to campaign, although none of them would be doing so together.

All this created challenges for the BBC News coverage because BBC editorial guidelines say that news programmes should not be led by the results of a single opinion poll. On the other hand, the government was clearly reacting to the results of the single poll, so news stories had to start with what the government was doing and mention the poll later on. It's a fine line to tread.

The day after the poll was published, I wrote a piece on the BBC News website called 'The perils of unprecedented polls', which discussed why it is so much more difficult to conduct meaningful opinion polls in one-off elections than it is for regular ones such as general elections.

In the end, Scotland remained part of the UK by 55 per cent to 45 per cent. There may have been other things going on, but it certainly looked as if the results of a single poll had led Cameron, Miliband and Clegg to drop everything and head to Scotland for a final push and to offer extra powers to the Scottish Parliament if the Scottish people voted to stay in the UK.

It's possible that on that Sunday the 'Yes' campaign was in the lead and drastic measures were needed. Alternatively, it may be that there was an overreaction to a 'Yes' lead within the margin of error when other polls still had 'No' ahead. We'll never know for sure, but worrying too much about a single poll is almost always a mistake.

This chapter will look at opinion polls around election times, and why you need to be careful with the results you see. In particular, I'll look at the key questions you need to ask that will help you work out what you can read into the poll:

- What can we learn from previous elections?

- How are exit polls different to regular opinion polls?

- What is the margin of error for an opinion poll?

What can we learn from previous elections?

Much of what you need to know about opinion polls is the same as the issues around surveys. In this case, you are trying to predict what will happen when everybody in the country is asked a question (but doesn't necessarily have to answer), i.e. you are trying to forecast the result of an election. Because you can't afford to ask everyone the question in advance, you ask a smaller number of people and hope they are representative of the people who are going to vote in the election.

You will generally see opinion polls asking at least 1000 people, and there is once again a key division between companies that carry out random sampling and those that have online panels. The difference is that the random samplers try to find ways to choose people such as randomly picking numbers out of the phone book. Pollsters using panels have thousands of names in a database of people who are prepared to complete polls for them and about whom they know a great deal. That means when they are asked to conduct a poll they can find a group of people they think are representative of the population. In both types of polling there can be adjustments made later on by the polling companies, and I will return to the challenges that this creates.

These methods have been developed largely through trial and error, based on the experiences of some of the classic mistakes in the history of polling. The first key case study is the 1936 US presidential election, when the incumbent Franklin D. Roosevelt was up against the Republican Governor of Kansas, Alfred Landon. One of the country's most widely respected magazines, the *Literary Digest*, which had correctly predicted the outcome of several previous elections, decided to conduct an enormous poll and got responses from about 2.4 million people. Just pause a moment to consider how large a poll that is – one of the largest ever conducted. But even that understates the process, because they sent dummy ballot papers to 10 million addresses. The amount of work involved is mind-boggling.

The weekly magazine created its mailing list based on lists such as all the telephone directories in the USA, country-club memberships and car registrations. It sent a ballot paper to each person on the list and asked them to complete and return it. A quarter of them did so, meaning that staff had to open and record the contents of 2.4 million letters. Based on those responses, the *Literary Digest* confidently predicted a victory to Alfred Landon by 57 per cent to 43 per cent. If you're wondering why you have heard of Roosevelt and not Landon, it is because the forecast was a staggering failure from one of the most expensive opinion polls ever conducted. In the event, Roosevelt won by 62 per cent to 38 per cent in one of the biggest landslides in a presidential election. It's a classic example of the fact that it doesn't matter how many people you ask if they're the wrong people.

Remember that this was the end of the Great Depression; there were still about nine million people unemployed in the United States, and owning a telephone or a car was a significant luxury. Making up the mailing list from phone books, country-club memberships and car registrations skewed the sample towards more affluent voters. It ignored those who were most likely to have been helped by Roosevelt's New Deal, which had brought the country out of the depression.

Also, only a quarter of the people who received the ballot in the post bothered to return it, and the people who could be bothered to return the ballot in the mail turned out not to be representative of the electorate as a whole.

The outcome of the 1936 election had been correctly predicted by George Gallup, who had used a quota system and a very considerably smaller sample, but he came unstuck in the 1948 presidential election between New York Governor Thomas Dewey and incumbent President Harry S. Truman. The idea of the quota system was to select characteristics of the population such as race, gender and age, and then make sure that the sample included the right proportions of such people. To get the sample of 3250 people polled, a professional interviewer would be told, for example, to find ten black women under the age of 40 living in a city. Beyond that, the interviewers were allowed to choose the people themselves. That element of human selection biased the sample again, with Gallup predicting a victory for the Republican Dewey by 50 per cent to 44 per cent (with the rest going to third party candidates) when in the event Truman won by 50 per cent to 45 per cent.

To be fair to Gallup, the other major pollsters of the time also predicted a win for Dewey, and Truman was widely considered to be the underdog in the election. The *Chicago Tribune* was so convinced that Dewey was going to win that it ran a headline in its early edition saying 'Dewey Defeats Truman'. The photo of Truman holding up the newspaper declaring victory for his opponent is one of the iconic moments in US political history. All the major pollsters were using the quota system. Presumably, at the time, Republicans were easier to find and interview than Democrats. It was also suggested that the poll was conducted too far in advance of the election. In the poll two weeks before election day, 15 per cent of the sample were undecided and it was assumed that their votes would split in the same way as those who had already decided. But Truman was good at campaigning in the last few days, so there may have been late decisions that did not show up in the poll. I'm always a bit suspicious of this though – the easiest defence if your opinion poll turns out to be wrong is to claim that voters changed their minds on election day.

The proportion of people undecided is an important thing to check when you're reading the results of a poll – it's the Whiskas effect. One of the best-known slogans in British advertising is that eight out of ten cats prefer Whiskas. But while the original advert for the cat food said that eight out of ten owners said their cats preferred it, I've seen references to the company being forced to change the line to reflect the fact that it was only eight out of ten cats whose owners expressed a preference. I have asked the Advertising Standards Authority to find that ruling for me and they couldn't, but the owners who don't express a preference are important. For all we know, 99 per cent of owners could have said their cats couldn't tell the difference between any types of canned meat, and the agency would have had to ask 1000 cat owners just to find 10 who could distinguish between brands.

Consider a situation in which a polling company interviews 1000 people and 300 of them say they will vote 'yes', 200 of them say they will vote 'no' and the rest say they haven't decided. If the reporter ignores the 'don't knows', the headline could be 'Yes leads in polls by 60 per cent to 40 per cent', but that would not really tell the current story of the election. Reporting that 'yes' was leading by 30 per cent to 20 per cent would much more accurately get across that there was still much to play for in the campaign.

This is an important decision in all surveys. It is often tempting to assume that people who say they don't know or have not yet decided would end up being like the rest of the population once they had made up their minds, but there is rarely evidence for this. Ignoring the undecided respondents is a misleading thing to do.

In the UK, one of the most famous times that the pollsters got it wrong was in 1992, when opinion polls consistently showed Labour leader Neil Kinnock slightly ahead of the Conservative incumbent Prime Minister John Major, with a hung parliament (in which no party has an overall majority) widely expected. The Conservatives had been in power for 13 years, there had just been a long recession and interest rates were above 10 per cent. Yet in the event, Major's Conservatives got more votes than any party before or since, won the popular vote by eight percentage points and retained a small majority in Parliament.

We never find out exactly why polls are wrong, but in this case the pollsters blamed three things. They suggested there had been a late swing to the Conservatives (which I've already said I'm suspicious about – the only evidence for that would be polling data, which feels like marking your own homework). They said that people had been reluctant to admit they were going to vote Conservative because it wasn't fashionable, a phenomenon known as 'Shy Tories'. And former YouGov president Peter Kellner suggested that there were sampling errors because the results of the 1991 census, which were published shortly after the 1992 election, showed there had been a sharper contraction in the working class and growth of the middle class during the 1980s than had been thought, which meant the sampling design used by the polling companies was skewed away from the Conservatives.

The outcome of the 2015 general election, when David Cameron's Conservatives unexpectedly took an overall majority, had also not been predicted by the polls. The polls were effectively predicting a dead heat, when the actual result was 36.9 per cent to the Conservatives and 30.4 per cent to Labour. The post-mortem into the polling at the election concluded that once again the problem had been with the sampling; that the polling companies had taken samples that unrepresentatively favoured Labour over the Conservatives and that adjustments made to the raw data had not solved this problem. The report also pointed out that while there had been polling at UK general elections in the past that was nearly as inaccurate as 2015, it hadn't received as much attention because it still managed to predict correctly which party would win.

The other growing problem for opinion polls, which I mentioned in the chapter about surveys, is that you have to phone an awful lot of people to get any of them to respond to your opinion poll, with one polling organisation saying that to get 2000 responses they were having to call about 30,000 random numbers. If a one-in-four response rate caused problems for the *Literary Digest* in 1936, a one-in-15 response rate must be a cause for concern. The people who are responding are unrepresentatively interested in talking to pollsters, which may well be introducing bias into the survey in other ways.

If the catchphrase to explain the 1992 errors was 'Shy Tories', in 2015 it was 'Lazy Labour', with the suggestion that people telling pollsters that they were going to vote Labour were less likely to turn out and vote than people who said they were going to vote Conservative. The pollsters also overestimated the likelihood of younger voters turning out. These are the sorts of things for which polling organisations try to adjust once they receive the raw data. It may be that you have heard from too few people of a particular age group or too few in a particular part of the country, for example, so you adjust your findings to reflect that, putting more weight on the responses you have received from under-represented groups. Then adjustments can be made for whether you think people are actually going to turn out to vote and even whether you think they are telling you the truth. The trouble is that such adjustments are based partly on experience from previous elections and partly on what the polling organisation thinks the outcome is likely to be. That may encourage group thinking among the pollsters, who could be tempted to adjust their results to make them tally with what their competitors are finding. That was not the case in 2017, when there was a much wider range of outcomes in the polls even if they did, on the whole, overstate the support for the Conservatives and underestimate Labour's support.

The experience from previous elections is important, which is why there are such severe challenges in one-off elections such as referendums. While you can have a pretty good guess how big the turnout will be in a general election, it is harder to predict, for example, how many people will vote on whether the voting system should be changed. It is also harder to know whether there is anything going on such as the Shy Tories or Lazy Labour phenomena in a referendum – is it going to be unfashionable to vote 'no' to Scottish Independence or 'yes' to Brexit? Also, as there are generally only two possible outcomes in a referendum, if you predict the wrong one, even if the result is really close, you are going to look bad.

I say there are only two possible outcomes, but I was asked about a possible third one when answering questions with the Reality Check team from listeners to BBC local radio stations during the EU referendum campaign. We spent a day in a radio studio in Westminster, answering questions for 20 minutes per station. It was fascinating, and the best question I was asked was what happens if the result is a dead heat. In an electorate of 46.5 million, of whom 33.6 million voted, it is staggeringly unlikely that there would be a draw, but staggeringly unlikely things do happen. I didn't know the answer so I asked to move on to the next question and said I would get back to them with an answer. But the answer is that there isn't one – there is nothing in place to answer the question of what happens if there's a draw. As the EU referendum was, strictly speaking, not binding, the government would just have had to decide what to do, but it would have been very embarrassing.

We know what happens if there is a draw in a local election – there was one for a seat on Northumberland County Council in 2017. In such circumstances it is down to the returning officer to decide how to break the tie. On this occasion, after two recounts, they decided to draw straws, but they could have chosen any random method such as tossing a coin or drawing names out of a hat. There are no such procedures in place for referendums.

In a general election, the prime minister is the person who can command a majority in the House of Commons, so a tie would not be a problem in the same way. Understanding the way an election works, whether it is just who gets the highest proportion of the popular vote or a first-past-the-post constituency system, is important.

How are exit polls different to regular opinion polls?

You may have noticed that there was not an exit poll at either the Scottish independence referendum or the EU referendum. An exit poll is different to a normal opinion poll because it is conducted by approaching people outside polling stations after they have voted. This means that the pollsters do not have to worry about whether or not the respondents are actually going to vote. The idea is to forecast the number of seats won by each party, as opposed to the national share of the vote. The exit polls you may have seen at UK general elections recently have been commissioned jointly by the BBC, ITV News and Sky News. The polling stations where the general election exit poll is conducted are carefully chosen based on past experience as the ones that give the best indication of which way the country as a whole will be voting. They speak to thousands of people (16,000 in 2010, for example) across a tiny proportion of the 39,000 polling stations across Britain – about 140 of them. It's a much bigger sample than you have in most opinion polls, but remember the lesson from 1936 that it doesn't matter how big the sample is if you're not getting the right people. The exit poll tends to be conducted in marginal seats, which change hands the most often, because that is where governments are made or broken.

The recent record of exit polls is pretty good, although they were wrong in predicting a hung parliament in 1992, just as the regular opinion polls had been. They had been less accurate in 1987, but still managed to predict the correct winner. The exit poll has done well in the last four general elections, getting the Labour majority right in 2005 and predicting a hung parliament with smaller support than expected for the Liberal Democrats in 2010. In 2015, it predicted much stronger support for the Conservatives than had been expected, although even it did not foresee the overall majority, but it did predict the huge rise in seats for the Scottish National Party and the collapse of Liberal Democrat support, which had former Lib Dem leader Paddy Ashdown saying he would publicly eat his hat if the exit poll was correct. He was later given a hat-shaped cake on *Question Time*. And in 2017 the exit poll predicted the smaller-than-expected support for the Conservatives.

The point about exit polls is that they try to establish the swing between parties. This is so that they can work out whether a particular party will do better or worse than it did last time based on what they are told by a proportion of voters at polling stations that have proved to be representative in the past. If, as in the case of referendums, you do not have the historical results to build an exit poll on, it is much harder to do and the risk of calling a two-horse race the wrong way is not worth taking.

It's also important to bear in mind that exit polls only speak to people who vote at polling stations so it will not take account of people voting by post.

What is the margin of error for an opinion poll?

Because polls are based on a sample, they have a margin of error, just as surveys do. In a properly random opinion poll based on 1000 responses, you can be 95 per cent confident that the margin of error will be plus or minus three percentage points. So if the poll finds that voters are evenly split on a 'yes' or 'no' question, it's likely that the actual response is somewhere between 53 per cent and 47 per cent in favour of 'yes'. Clearly, therefore, if you are looking at a close-run contest, you shouldn't read too much into a lead of one or two percentage points, as was the case with the Scottish referendum poll mentioned earlier.

That margin of error comes down to plus or minus two percentage points if you poll 2000 people. But this assumes that the way you are sampling is accurate and that no sampling biases have crept in. If it turns out that only a quarter of people contacted actually responded to the poll, or supporters of one side in the election were much more enthusiastic to talk about it, or key groups of supporters of one side were particularly difficult to get hold of, then the margin of error could be considerably greater. Also, the process of weighting the raw data to increase the impact of under-represented groups increases the margin of error.

Strictly speaking, these margins of error only refer to polls using random samples and not panels. For a sample to be random, every member of the population being surveyed must have an equal chance of being part of the sample. With online panels we know this is not the case because not everybody has internet access and the panels rely on people opting into the process rather than being chosen randomly. Companies that conduct such polls are experimenting with alternative ways of getting across the level of uncertainty.

Also, do make sure that the poll you're reading has been conducted by a reasonably reputable organisation, which has a code of conduct that prevents the worst abuses of polling; like surveys, this includes wording questions in a way that will mislead respondents or encourage them to answer in a particular way. The polls commissioned during an election period by national newspapers will often be conducted by British Polling Council members, who should be transparent about the way they conduct their polls. Polling companies seem to behave themselves better during election campaigns when their reputations are on the line.

The BBC never conducts polls asking people how they plan to vote, but it is one of the broadcasters that commissions the general election exit poll, which asks people how they just voted.

So the message is, if you have seen several reputable polls that suggest one side is leading by about 70 per cent to 30 per cent, you can be pretty confident that side is going to win. The exit poll for the Irish vote on legalising abortion was pretty conclusive although, as discussed, conducting an exit poll was a risky thing to do. If you have seen several polls calling it as 51 per cent to 49 per cent in either direction then you would be best off concluding that the outcome is too close to call and there is not a lot else that opinion polls can tell you about this particular contest.

This was the case with the EU referendum – in the days leading up to the vote there was no consistent picture, with some polls giving Remain a slight lead, some giving Leave a slight lead and some having the two neck and neck. It is frustrating that polls aren't more helpful in a close contest, but they are not and it is important to recognise that they are not. That is why BBC Editorial Guidelines (which are publicly available to read online) indicate that staff should be suspicious of them.

The lesson from historical elections is that taking accurate samples to test opinion during an election campaign is difficult, with pitfalls including asking loads of people but excluding big sections of society; letting pollsters choose who they want to interview; and ignoring ways in which supporters of each side may differ, such as whether they are more or less likely to tell you for whom they are going to vote or whether they will turn out on polling day.

Knowing how the poll was conducted helps you test whether it was robust and whether the questions asked were sensible and clear. Also, make sure you know what the organisers have done about undecided voters – just ignoring them and assuming they will end up being the same as the rest of the population is misleading.

Finally, try not to let your own decision on whether or how to vote be influenced by polls, especially ones where the gap between the parties is close to the margin of error – you will regret it if they turn out not to be accurate.

CHAPTER 3

Cost

Bear in mind that costings are bogus

Picture the scene: it's a bit snowy in London. Not snowy in a way that people from places with proper weather such as Canada or Norway or Scotland would be concerned about, but there are a few inches of snow on the ground.

Parts of the transport system have ground to a halt, but you have nonetheless managed to fight your way into work. Whatever you may think of journalists, imagine you have walked miles through the snow to get to the office of the newspaper where you work and you have made it just in time for your morning editorial meeting.

Your editor, a wizened old hack, stares out of the window and says: 'It's pretty snowy out there. I bet that's costing the economy a pretty penny.' And he turns to you and tells you to go and find out how much it has cost.

This has been the experience of many a reporter. It is a knee-jerk reaction for editors to ask how much things cost. Let's look at an example from the *Daily Telegraph* on 2 February 2009, not because it's any worse than many other versions of this story, but because it shows its workings well.

It has the headline: 'Snow Britain: disruption could cost UK economy £3bn'. The figures come from the Federation of Small Businesses (FSB), which has apparently warned that the snow would make the UK economy lose out by £1.2 billion on Monday and Tuesday, with smaller losses in the rest of the week, making the total up to £3 billion.

How has that figure been worked out? The article explains that the FSB: 'made the calculation based on the assumption that 20 per cent of the workforce or 6.4 million people were off work on Monday because of the weather conditions, and that an average bank holiday costs the UK economy £6bn'.

The economists think that a bank holiday costs £6 billion, because they made that number up previously – we'll come back to it – and they know that nobody works on bank holidays at all, which may come as a surprise to any journalist or indeed nurse, police officer, supermarket worker, transport worker . . . It's not clear where the figure of 20 per cent of people not making it to work comes from, but the economists have decided that one-fifth of people not making it to work will mean the snow will cost 20 per cent of the amount a bank holiday costs.

Do we believe this? The cost of snow is an excellent example of the dubious costings that editors seem to love. I've been fighting against them for years. In this chapter we will be looking at why any headline showing the cost of something is likely to be bogus. Remember, I'm talking about the cost of things, not the price. There is no question that if I go and buy a chocolate bar at the local shop I will know what the price is – it's there on the shelf. But how much it has cost to get that chocolate bar on the shelf is another question and it is not an exact science.

This chapter will go through three things you need to understand whenever you see figures for cost:

- What is meant by cost to the economy?

- Are we talking about the total cost or the extra cost?

- Questionable costings in business

What is meant by cost to the economy?

Back to the cost of snow. When we left our calculation, we were considering whether £6 billion is a reasonable costing for a bank holiday. If you added up everything produced in the UK economy to generate a figure for gross domestic product (GDP), you would get about £2 trillion a year. There are about 252 working days a year, so that's getting on for £8 billion a day, although it was closer to £6 billion a day when the *Telegraph*'s article was published in 2009.

Does it make sense to see a bank holiday as an almost total loss of output to the economy? One of the fundamental problems of the UK economy at the moment is low productivity – that's the amount produced by workers per hour – so maybe giving people a day off every now and then would help them work more effectively the rest of the time. Also, bank holidays are a jolly good thing for some parts of the economy. If you're selling ice creams on Margate beach you would laugh at the idea that having a bank holiday would lose your business money.

So, we've started with a dubious number, divided it by five, and that's how much snow has cost the economy. But there's an even more serious problem with this calculation, which is the assumption that snow is bad for the economy at all. Just as bank holidays are probably going to be good for people selling ice cream, so snow also has its economic upsides (though probably not for ice-cream sellers).

When we talk about things being good or bad for an economy we are talking about whether they will increase or decrease the level of GDP, which is the measure of the total amount produced in the economy. It's clear that there are some parts of the economy that will lose out as a result of the snow. If you are running a car plant in Sunderland on three shifts a day and you lose a shift because your workers cannot get in or parts cannot be delivered, then that is going to be a dead loss for you.

But not much of the UK economy is like that – 79 per cent of the UK's GDP comes from the service sector. If you are a hairdresser and you cannot open on Monday or Tuesday, the people whose appointments were cancelled will still need haircuts. You may need to work a bit of overtime in the following week or so, but you are not going to lose the whole two days of takings. More and more people can work from home, even if their children's schools are closed due to snow. It's not that people failing to get to work isn't a problem for the economy – if you're selling sandwiches to office staff in a city centre you will be likely to make less money that day, and your customers will be unlikely to eat extra lunch in the coming days to make up for it. But it's not as much of a problem for the economy as it was when the UK was more dependent on manufacturing.

Now look at the benefits to GDP from snow. If councils pay people extra to spread grit and clear roads, that's a boost to GDP. In fact, some of the rock salt that is used to grit roads is mined in places such as Cheshire and County Antrim, and having lots of that bought by councils is particularly good for the economy.

Also, if people have to stay at home there are more opportunities for online shopping, which will boost the economy. Sales of winter clothing would be expected to increase, and the extra spending on heating during the cold spell would also be good news for GDP.

Imagine people crash their cars in the icy conditions. They might take the car round to the local garage and pay to have it fixed. If an insurance company has to pay out that would be a transfer of money that might otherwise go to shareholders who would be marginally less likely to spend it, so that's good for the economy too. And if the car is written off and the owner uses the insurance to buy a new one, well maybe that will help the factory in Sunderland to cope with losing a shift.

I have occasionally talked on my statistics courses about the benefits to the economy of increased demand for replacement hips when people slip on ice. The manufacture of replacement hips is a great British hi-tech industry. I have been accused of being callous, which is missing the point. What is good for the economy is not necessarily good for people.

You could suggest that all this is more of an argument for why GDP is a bad measure of what is going on in the economy than anything about snow. If you crash your car and have to pay someone to return it to its previous condition, should that really be seen as a benefit to the economy? The point is that some aspects of snow boost GDP and some are bad for it, and it's very hard to tell on the day the snow falls which will be the case.

If snow had a significant effect on the economy then you would expect the Office for National Statistics (ONS) to mention it when it publishes its quarterly GDP figures. In the first quarter of 2009 it didn't mention it at all, so we can assume that the snow did not cost the economy £3 billion.

The following year, there was heavy snow in the week before Christmas, and that was a big deal – a perfect storm if you like. People could not get to the shops to buy gifts, and office parties in bars and restaurants were cancelled. That delay in purchases was significant because if you buy things in the week before Christmas they are more likely to be at full price, whereas if you buy them after Christmas they are more likely to be discounted (as well as too late).

Also, because the snow was right at the end of the year, even money lost to the economy that was later made up (i.e. people going to the hairdresser the following week) would have gone into the GDP figures for the first quarter of 2011. They could turn up even later – the part of the ONS that calculates the GDP figures delayed its own Christmas party until the following April, so that would have turned up in the figures for the second quarter. It's not often that Christmas parties boost second-quarter growth.

For the last quarter of 2010, the ONS did indeed acknowledge the damage done by the snow. It said that the weather had knocked about half a percentage point off that quarter's GDP, which is a considerable hit. Half a percentage point off a quarter's growth is just over £2 billion, so even the weather event that was bad enough to be mentioned by the ONS did not reach the £3 billion mark.

In 2018, the UK once again had enough snow in London to dominate the national news agenda for a few days, when the 'Beast from the East' swept in from Siberia. The front page of the *Observer* on 4 March carried the headline: 'Freezing weather costs UK economy £1bn a day'. That's a nice, round number, exactly the same as the amount that the *Daily Telegraph* said it was costing in December 2010 in its headline: 'UK snow: bad weather costing economy £1bn a day'.

That's actually not a great coincidence as both figures came from the same source, the Centre for Economics and Business Research (CEBR) in 2010 and its founder Doug McWilliams in 2018. He tweeted that total output each day would be cut by 20 per cent, even after the effects of online shopping, working from home and a 20 per cent increase in energy output were taken into account. He described it as 'a very rough estimate' and told me he expected a lot of it to be made up by the end of the quarter this time round. But if it's going to be made up then it's not being lost to the economy at all – delayed spending is still spending.

Nonetheless, for only the second time, the ONS did indeed mention snow in its GDP report. Its report said: 'While some impacts on GDP from the snow in the first quarter of 2018 have been recorded for construction and retail sales, the effects were generally small, with very little impact observed in other areas of the economy.' So still not £1 billion a day then.

The problem here is not so much the way that the FSB or indeed the CEBR went about calculating the cost of snow, it's that the question was asked at all. When snow falls there seems to be a strong urge in the minds of editors to think about costs to the economy, despite the lack of evidence that there is one. It is extraordinary that a single tweet from a single economist would be enough to create the front-page headline on a national newspaper, especially when it was the same headline run by a rival newspaper eight years before.

This is not just about snow, it goes for any events and their cost to the economy: fires, earthquakes, train strikes – we do not know on the day how much they will cost the economy. I was particularly shocked at the interviews being done after the Asian tsunami on Boxing Day 2004, when questions were being asked about how much it would cost the economy when we were not even close to an accurate figure for the hundreds of thousands of people who had been killed. The cost to the economy was not the story. Also, as aid pours into relatively poor parts of the world to fund reconstruction work, the economy gets a boost, which may even make up for the immediate loss of economic output at the time, but that does not make it any less of a disaster.

In the case of events that are important to the insurance industry such as flooding in the developed world, the industry may come up with an early estimate of how much it expects to pay out, which is a more useful number than the cost to the economy, but it's still a very rough estimate.

Figures that you hear on the day of an event for how much it is costing the economy are not reasonably likely to be true. That's the case wherever you are in the world, even places where snow is expected and planned for.

It's not as if there aren't numbers available that would make more sense. The owner of the café on the corner could tell the nation how much they reckon they have lost as a result of people not getting into work. Maybe they would say how many fewer coffees they have sold than they would normally have done by that time of day. That number of coffees has the advantage of probably being an accurate figure, allowing the audience to get a handle on the idea that some people are losing money and not being a meaninglessly big number such as £3 billion, which the brain can't really process anyway. And also it's not just been plucked out of the air.

Are we talking about the total cost or the extra cost?

Bogus costing is not just a problem in news headlines. To illustrate why, consider what happened to me in Egypt in 1990.

When I was 16 I went on a walking tour of the Sinai Desert with the Israeli nature protection society. I had a great time until about four days in when, at the bottom of a valley, I slipped down a gap between two boulders and broke my right ankle very badly. While forms of mobile communication did exist, they were banned in Sinai by the Egyptian authorities, presumably in case anyone wanted to spy on their desert. We sent part of the group off for the four-hour walk to the nearest telephone and another part walked off to the next campsite to bring back supplies. We had a medic with us, but the strongest painkiller he had was paracetamol, which wasn't really strong enough for the situation.

When the group reached the telephone they called the United Nations at Taba, on the Israeli border. They said they would love to come and collect me, but I'd clearly need winching out of the valley and they didn't have any helicopters capable of winching. The only people in Sinai who did have such helicopters were the Multinational Force and Observers (MFO), which was a set of peacekeeping troops in southern Sinai set up as part of the Camp David Agreement. My friends suggested the UN might like to call the MFO, but the problem was the UN did not recognise the MFO, so a French major in Taba had to call a Russian general in Cairo to get permission to call the MFO down the road.

They eventually got permission and the MFO said they would be delighted to come and rescue me, but it was getting dark and it would be a dangerous mission at night, so they would turn up in the morning.

The following day, 19 hours after I'd broken my leg, two helicopters turned up at my valley. They had needed to call out a second one because, by the time they had found me, the first helicopter didn't have enough fuel left for winching me out. Two US Army medics were dropped off at the top of the valley with a metal stretcher and sent down to strap me into it. They introduced themselves as 'Bob and Dean from Pennsylvania and Alabama, that fine southern state'. I was obviously pleased to see them, and as a Royal Air Force cadet I was beyond excited at the idea of being winched into a US Army 'Huey' helicopter. Bob told me to keep my eyes shut as I was winched so I didn't get sand in them, but that was never going to happen. It was an odd sensation, which reminded me of the bit in the first Superman film when our hero catches Lois Lane in mid-air and says, 'Easy miss, I've got you,' and she says 'You have got me – who's got you?' When I got into the helicopter, all the soldiers thanked me for giving them something interesting to do that day. Apparently I'd got them out of a boring training exercise. It takes a very special person to save your life and then thank you for the opportunity to do so.

If you have ever watched a Vietnam War film you'll know what a Huey – the nickname for a Bell UH-1 Iroquois – is like. In particular, the sides tend to be open. I was perfectly safe because my stretcher was attached to the floor, but nobody had mentioned that to me, so the banked turns were a bit scary. They took me to an excellent hospital in Eilat in the south of Israel, with the only further incident being that we were aggressively challenged by a US Navy battleship that described us as an unidentified aircraft. This was summer 1990 and the Gulf War was just kicking off, so there was a certain amount of nervousness in the area. The pilot who said we had been challenged by the US Navy also said that everyone should duck.

So why am I telling you my teenage adventure story in a book about statistics? Well, when I got back to school, somebody asked how much the US Army had charged for rescuing me. When I told him the army hadn't charged at all, he said that was very generous. Don't get me wrong, I owe my life to the wonderful servicemen who rescued me from that desert (not to mention my tour group who so willingly helped in so many ways), but how generous was the US military being?

Let's try making a shopping list of what it cost to rescue a foolhardy British tourist from the middle of the Sinai Desert. You start with the cost of two helicopters for a day, which is seriously expensive. I know that because my father had been rescued by helicopter after a skiing accident three years previously (my poor mother . . .) and our insurance did have to pay for that one. That rescue and treatment almost broke through the limit for our travel insurance, so we know helicopters are properly pricey – my family is very much in profit over travel insurance providers. On top of the helicopters themselves, we needed at least three tanks of fuel, because the Huey I was in had to stop to refuel near Eilat so it could return to base. Then there was personnel: a pilot and co-pilot for each helicopter, plus Bob and Dean, and there were at least two other soldiers looking after me in the back of the Huey, so that's at least eight highly trained people, working for most of the day, not to mention the support staff back at base who kept them in the air. And they used a whole lot of splints, bandages and drips when they were patching me up. If you add all of that up you have to be getting into six figures for the cost of saving my life. Well worth it, I'd say, but would the US taxpayer agree?

Now, let's think about this another way. All of the staff involved were going to be working that day anyway. The funding of the MFO is established by international treaties and I'm not sure there's any allowance for some of it to be refunded by the insurance companies employed by British teenagers. If they hadn't come to rescue me that day, the helicopters and fuel were due to be used up in an exercise. Instead, they were used on a mission, which from talking to the soldiers seemed to have improved morale – apparently being posted to Sharm El Sheikh was a bit boring. So the only extra cost to the US taxpayer was some medical supplies.

Depending on how you think about it, the cost of rescuing me was either hundreds of thousands of pounds or almost nothing with a boost to troop morale thrown in. These two ways of thinking about the cost of something are known as the total cost and the marginal cost. The marginal cost is the extra cost of doing something so, in this case, it's the cost of a few medical supplies. The total cost is the hundreds of thousands of pounds it would have cost to rescue me out of the desert if all the equipment and personnel and fuel hadn't been going to be used that day anyway.

This is an important distinction and you'll spot it in the news all the time. A regular favourite is how much the security is going to cost for a demonstration. You may well need 100 police officers to attend, but what would they have been doing if they hadn't been doing that? Are they all coming in on their days off and being paid overtime, or is covering marches just part of their job? Should you take the total cost of the barriers and other equipment used and divide it by the number of times you think the equipment will be required, or do you just decide that's something the police have to own anyway? If you wanted to make a particular police operation sound expensive it would be easy to pile up the costs, but you could also make it look negligible if you wanted, and that is why all figures you see for costs are at the very least questionable.

We saw estimates of anything from £2m to £30m for how much the security cost for the Royal Wedding in 2018 between Prince Harry and Meghan Markle, but bear in mind when you see those that police forces can apply for extra funding from the Home Office for dealing with events that are outside their usual remit. Thames Valley Police, which provided security for the event in Windsor, is not awash with cash, so it could be forgiven for billing for its total costs rather than its marginal costs. But that does not mean it is reasonable to say that the event cost the police that amount.

Every now and then we get a figure from the National Health Service (NHS) for how much each missed appointment costs it. In January 2018 we were told by the *Guardian* that missed appointments cost the NHS in England a nice round £1 billion a year. That was based on eight million outpatient appointments being missed at a cost of £120 each. The money could instead have been spent on 250,000 hip-replacement operations, we were told. To be clear, it's important to turn up for appointments in the NHS, but that doesn't make it OK to use misleading stats.

The £120 per appointment figure comes from taking the total cost of having outpatient services in the NHS and dividing it by the number of appointments. But for a missed appointment to cost the NHS £120 you have to assume that all the doctors, nurses and support staff will be sitting around doing nothing during the scheduled time for that appointment (although they will still be consuming the sort of single-use equipment that will come under the average cost). In reality, the NHS will almost certainly bear in mind when scheduling appointments that a certain number of people will not turn up. And even if they didn't, I can't remember the last time I saw a doctor or nurse who didn't look like they were doing anything useful and couldn't use a few minutes to catch up with themselves. So missed appointments probably don't cost the NHS very much at all – in fact, it would probably struggle to cope if everybody did turn up. It certainly wouldn't be able to pay for an extra quarter of a million replacement hips.

Costings are dangerous things because it is easy to make something look cheap or expensive depending on how you work them out. Costings are most often used to make things look expensive, so whenever you see an impressively big price tag being attached to something, just ask whether any of the costs would have had to be paid anyway.

Questionable costings in business

The ambiguities around costings also affect the world of business. Costs are clearly a crucial figure on any balance sheet. Imagine I have a company producing cuddly seal toys. I have rented some space on a factory floor, bought some sewing machines, taken on some machinists and bought in supplies of stuffing, cotton, synthetic fur and plastic features. Now I need to work out how much it costs to produce each cuddly seal. Much of this is obvious – I know how much I have paid for the amount of material I need for each seal. I have a good idea how long it takes each of my employees to make a seal and I know how much I am paying them per hour. But then there are trickier questions. I don't really know how many seals can be made with each sewing machine before it wears out so I need to guess. I could decide that I would expect a sewing machine to last a year, or five years, or ten years. Whichever one I choose will make a big difference to how much of the cost of the machines I add to the cost of each seal, which means that it makes a big difference to how much profit I make on each seal.

These calculations go into my company's management accounts, which is what I use to run my company. The other set of figures are my financial accounts, which is what I publish, using various complicated accounting regulations and arbitrary assumptions to try to make my company's results comparable with other businesses. These are the figures you will read about when companies publish their annual results. Companies have auditors to prevent them doing misleading things in their financial accounts, but even within what is allowed there is considerable wriggle-room. For example, in the financial crisis, financial institutions were giving very different valuations to the same assets, even though they were often being audited by the same big accountancy firms. There have also been famous cases of now-bankrupt companies having fiddled their figures by declaring items that should clearly have been operating expenses as some sort of multi-year investment.

My cuddly-seal-making company is very simple, so it's pretty clear when you take a step back whether the way I'm running it is reasonable. But most companies are more complicated than that, and the management software and accounting systems that they now use make it more difficult to spot things that in retrospect are clearly misleading.

There is no question that there are ambiguities in costs and valuations for companies. Consider the example of a company that owns a railway carriage. What value do you give the carriage in your accounts? It could be the amount that it would cost you to replace it with a new one, or at least a second-hand one, which would make it a valuable asset. Or you could take into account how much it would cost you to scrap it at the end of its life, which could make it a liability.

The costs really matter when a business is trying to take decisions. Imagine that the zoo is getting some polar bears, and they put out a tender for cuddly polar bear toys. My company producing the cuddly seal toys decides it might diversify and bids for the contract. How much does it cost me to make a cuddly polar bear? More of the synthetic fur, stuffing and plastic features will be needed, so I definitely have to include them in the cost. And I'll need to hire a couple of extra staff, so that is part of the cost. But there is time during the day when not all my sewing machines are being used, so they can be used to make the polar bears – do I include a proportion of the costs of the sewing machines in my final figure? And what about me? I'm having to devote some of my time to this, so perhaps I should allocate a proportion of my wages to the cost of the polar bears. I won't need to get any more factory space or spend any more on heating or lighting, but should I allocate any of those costs to the new product? The trouble is that if I keep producing new products without allocating any of my overheads to them then I will probably end up bankrupting the company. But if I allocate too many of my overheads then I won't win the contract to supply the toys. So I will come up with an amount it costs me to produce a cuddly polar bear and base my offer to the zoo on that figure, but it is important not to see that figure as some sort of scientific fact – it could have come anywhere on a wide range of costs.

In reality, I will probably take the additional costs of producing the polar bears and add a percentage to cover my existing overheads (for example, management, buildings and research costs that are not allocated to any particular product) to get a minimum price at which I can afford to sell. But there is another important concept here, which is sunk costs. My father used to give the example for sunk costs of the flower stall he used to walk past on his way home from work. Imagine this flower stall is only open on weekdays and does not have a way of keeping cut flowers fresh over the weekend. My father walked past this stall when it was about to close on a Friday afternoon and thought that he might buy my mother some flowers. Consider a bunch of roses that was being sold for £10. The stallholder paid £5. If Dad offered him £5 for the flowers it would make sense to accept it to avoid making a loss. What about if he offered £3? It feels like the stallholder should decline that because he would be making a loss, but in fact the £5 he paid for the flowers is a sunk cost – the money is gone and there is no way to get it back, so he should accept £3 for the roses. And nothing says romantic gift like economic theory and cut-price flowers.

In my cuddly-toy business, if the bottom suddenly falls out of the seal market and I'm left owning lots of white fur that I can't do anything with, I might offer to sell the polar bear toys more cheaply to limit my losses from the sunk costs, even if that means I have to sell the toys for less than it's costing me to make them. Selling them cheaply may mean that I lose less money than I would if I did not manufacture them at all.

Bidding for a polar bear contract is simple, but imagine if you're bidding for a contract to do something complicated such as building a bridge, when all of the costs are estimates because there are all sorts of unknowns. It may turn out that the bridge takes much longer to build than expected because of bad weather, or perhaps there will turn out to be an unexploded Second World War bomb found on the site. With so much uncertainty, it is very difficult to predict the costs of big projects accurately.

Take the London 2012 Olympic Games. When decisions were being taken about whether to bid to host the games, the people coming up with the costings had very little idea of what the eventual games would look like. The costs started at anywhere between £2.5 billion and £3.8 billion, but the games ended up costing closer to £9 billion. There is widespread support for the idea of evidence-based policymaking, but if the evidence is completely wrong, is it still a good idea? I asked someone who had been a senior civil servant at the time, and they said it was OK that the costings were wrong because everybody knew they were wrong. That is a very odd basis on which to make a decision. If everyone knows the costings are wrong then should the government just come out and say that the event will cost loads but it still thinks it would be a good idea?

The UK government did not face the same problems that the Swiss authorities had with trying to host the 2022 or 2026 Winter Olympics in the resorts of Davos and St Moritz. In each case, there had to be a referendum to decide whether to bid to host the games. I attended one of the events that was trying to persuade locals in Davos to support the idea and there was clearly a major charm offensive going on. In the end, local people rejected the idea of hosting the games in either year, with the way that costs always spiral from the initial estimates being cited as one of the key concerns among voters. I wonder if a referendum on whether to bid to host the London 2012 Olympics would have been successful.

The trouble with taking decisions about big, expensive projects is that you have to come up with a cash value for the benefits as well. In the case of the Olympics that involves a lot of tricky intangibles, such as inspiring the public to take more exercise. To take another example, the costing for the HS2 high-speed rail line between London and Birmingham and then Manchester and Leeds was particularly closely scrutinised, especially when it turned out that the benefits of it were based on the assumption that time spent on trains is completely lost time for businesspeople. Supporters of the line could claim that as it was going to cut half an hour off the journey time from London to Birmingham, it was reasonable to take the value of half an hour of the working time of all the business people using the service and add that to the benefits to the economy. But that is not really acceptable, because as long as you get a seat it is perfectly possible to do productive work on a train. Again, there is considerable guesswork involved in these figures. All big government spending decisions are based on such high-risk figures – does this make evidence-based policymaking a waste of time? I hope it doesn't but it is important to be aware of the uncertainty about any of the predicted costs or benefits.

How does any of this help you? You can avoid being misled by remembering to treat any claims involving cost with caution. Remember that costs for business and big projects are inexact. Once you have grasped the amount of room for manoeuvre with costings, you can think about incentives. Look at who is coming up with the estimate of how much something is going to cost and think about whether they would have any reason to want to make it look more expensive or less expensive. Would the headline writers like to have a bigger figure for the cost of snow or a smaller one? Would a government trying to launch a big project rather it looked more expensive or less expensive?

Once you have considered incentives and asked whether any of the costs would have been incurred anyway, you will be well on the way to grasping how much credence you should give to the costing in front of you.

CHAPTER 4

Percentages
Beware of lonely percentages

Percentages are a really useful tool, which can be used either to help or hinder people's understanding of numbers. Percentages are taught as part of the primary-school maths programme and I reckon most people you know will claim to understand them. But they are also the bit of maths I have been most surprised to find that colleagues have been unable to carry out.

Early in my career I worked for Reuters Financial Television, which made fairly pointy-headed economics and business programmes for City professionals to watch at their desks. I was programme editor for a show called *Equities Briefing*, which covered news about companies. It was a good, fun programme to make and colleagues were enthusiastic about working on it, especially after I introduced compulsory lunch breaks. One particular freelancer's job for the programme involved writing short pieces about company announcements, generally their results. We always included whether their profits before tax had gone up or down and the percentage change. Five minutes before the programme was due to start on her first day I looked at her script, which was excellent, except that it said the profits had gone up by x per cent – there was no number given. It was at this point that she admitted that despite having an economics-based degree, she could not work out a percentage change. Her memory of the incident is that I did not get cross (I'm glad to say) but instead we would work out the percentage changes together every morning as the director counted down to the programme.

She was not alone in struggling with percentages, but they are pretty simple really and very important in understanding the numbers around us. In this chapter I will go through:

- How to work out percentages

- How to tell if someone is trying to mislead you with percentages

- Compound interest and how it can help you understand big percentage changes

How to work out percentages

My colleague at Reuters went on to be very successful, I hope in part due to her newfound skill with percentages. Lots of people don't understand percentages, but most of them are not big enough to admit it. There are not many sums in this book, but when it comes to percentages there seems to be such a gap between the number of people who claim to be able to cope with them and those who actually can, that I am going to put the method here (nobody ever has to know whether you needed to read it). I see many colleagues using percentage calculators online now, and there's nothing wrong with that – we're not under exam conditions here. But there is something to be said for understanding how it's done from scratch – I think knowing the mechanics helps you develop a sense of when a number feels wrong.

There are three types of percentages you're likely to come across:

1. What is x per cent of this number?
   The comedy rock band Half Man Half Biscuit made a classic song called '99 Per Cent of Gargoyles Look Like Bob Todd', named after the actor who appeared alongside comedians such as Benny Hill. Milan's Duomo, which apparently has more statues than any other building in the

world, has 96 gargoyles (a distorted carved figure only counts as a 'gargoyle' if it is used to channel rainwater away from the building, otherwise it's a simply a grotesque). If you wanted to find out how many of the gargoyles on Milan's cathedral look like Bob Todd, and you accept that Half Man Half Biscuit's percentage is correct, you would start by working out 99/100, which is 0.99. Then multiply that by the number of gargoyles, 96, and you would discover that 95 of them look like Bob Todd.

2. What percentage is this number of that number? Returning to the Whiskas slogan that I mentioned in Chapter 2, if eight out of ten cats prefer it, what is that as a percentage? To work out the percentage, calculate 8/10, which is 0.8, and then multiply by 100 to get the answer: 80 per cent.

3. What is the percentage change in a figure? This is the one that catches out many people, certainly my assistant producer at Reuters Financial Television. There were 380 goals scored in the UEFA Champions League in 2016–17 and 401 goals scored in 2017–18. If you want to find out what that is as a percentage increase, subtract the old number from the new number (401 minus 380) to get the increase of 21 goals. Then divide that by the old number and multiply the

answer by 100 (this is where mistakes happen – people often divide by the new number). So that's 21/380 × 100, which is 5.5 per cent. So there has been a 5.5 per cent increase in the number of goals scored in the Champions League. If you want to try an exercise by yourself, there were 347 goals scored in the Champions League in 2015–16. Work out the percentage change between 2015–16 and 2016–17. The answer will be at the end of the chapter.

Staying on the football theme, people often get upset about players referring to themselves as having given 110 per cent, which annoys people because it is not possible. I'm usually at the front of the queue when it comes to numerical pedantry, but this one doesn't bother me so much because, firstly, we all know what they mean and, secondly, they could mean they are giving 110 per cent of the amount of effort they had given in the previous game, which is perfectly possible.

But it does introduce percentages over 100, which can be tricky. Take the headlines in 2017 about the cryptocurrency Bitcoin. In the first nine months of the year, the value of the currency rose from about $1000 to about $5000. What would you say the percentage change had been? You can go back to the method above and check before I tell you, if you like.

OK – it had gone up by 400 per cent. If you thought it was 500 per cent then you are not alone. Almost everybody on my statistics courses makes that mistake.

Remember, $1000 is 100 per cent of the original value.

$1000 to $2000 is a rise of $1000, so it's a rise of 100 per cent.

$3000 would be a rise of 200 per cent.

$4000 would be a rise of 300 per cent.

$5000 is a rise of 400 per cent.

What this tells us is that people just do not understand percentages over 100 per cent. What they do understand is multiples, so you're much better off saying the value of Bitcoin increased fivefold or by five times, and everyone will understand what you mean.

And before you dash out and buy a Bitcoin, bear in mind that the currency went on to a valuation above $19,000 in December 2017 before crashing to below $7000 in February 2018, so not one for widows and orphans.

Another pitfall to avoid when you're dealing with percentages is the difference between a percentage increase and a percentage point increase. This is important when you're comparing two percentages.

So, for example, imagine that you took an exam and you only received a mark of 25 per cent. You decided to take it again and this time you got 50 per cent. You could either say that your score in the exam has increased by 100 per cent (because it's doubled) or by 25 percentage points (from 25 per cent to 50 per cent). It's important not to confuse the two.

If you took the exam a third time and were given a mark of 55 per cent, how much better would you have done? Well, your score has gone up by five percentage points, from 50 per cent to 55 per cent. But you could also say that your score had gone up by 10 per cent, because five is 10 per cent of 50.

In November 2017, the Bank of England raised interest rates from 0.25 per cent to 0.50 per cent. This was widely reported as an increase of 0.25 per cent, which is wrong – it was an increase of 100 per cent (because it doubled) or 0.25 percentage points. Hardly anyone ran the headline 'interest rates double', as tempting as that might have been. You might also have heard it referred to as going up by 25 basis points or 25 bps. A basis point is financial jargon for 0.01 per cent.

Another conceptual difficulty with percentages is that they are not the same going down and coming up – if something falls 50 per cent and then rises 50 per cent it doesn't end up back where it started. If I buy a share that costs £1 and it falls 50 per cent then it will be worth 50p. If it then rises 50 per cent then it will be worth 75p. This is a particular hazard when you're following something that has fallen very sharply and then had a tiny recovery. It may have fallen so far that the tiny recovery is huge in percentage terms.

A good example of this is sales of vinyl records. Vinyl sales peaked in the 1970s when shipments reached about 90 million a year. This is shipments, not sales – if records were sent to shops and then not sold they would still appear on these figures. Also, it's the number of vinyl discs, so a double album would count as two. This might be a problem if the trend were ambiguous, but it's not – vinyl shipments fell from the late 1970s until the early 1990s and then collapsed to below one million. Falling from about 90 million to below one million a year is a drop of about 99 per cent, with first the CD and then downloads and streaming hitting the preferred medium of decades of rockers. The British Phonographic Industry (BPI), which represents the UK's recorded-music industry, started recording vinyl sales properly without the above caveats in 1994, charting their fall from about 1.5 million sales that year to about 200,000 in 2007. But then the recovery began, with sales passing one million again in 2014 and reaching 4.1 million in 2017. You could say that vinyl sales had fallen 99 per cent and then risen 1900 per cent, which would make it sound as if vinyl sales had gone through the roof and unprecedented numbers of records were being sold. Of course, that isn't the case. While the recovery in vinyl sales has been extraordinary, we are still very considerably below the level of 1970s peak vinyl, when 90 million discs were being shipped. Percentages are bigger on the way up than they are on the way down because nothing can fall by more than 100 per cent. You may be able to give 110 per cent of the effort you gave in last week's match, but you definitely can't give 110 per cent less than you did last time.

Now you know how to work out percentages and percentage changes, you know that you need to avoid percentages over 100, and you understand the difference between a percentage change and a percentage point change. You realise that percentages are bigger on the way up than on the way down, and you know how many of the gargoyles on Milan's Duomo look like Bob Todd. Armed with this knowledge, you can now start challenging some of the percentages reported in the news and get a feeling for when you might be being misled.

How to tell if someone is trying to mislead you with percentages

When you see figures only being given in percentages – what I call lonely percentages – you need to think about whether this has been done for a reason and whether the absolute numbers would tell you a different story. In the vinyl example, if you wanted to make it sound as if vinyl sales were back to their peak then you would just talk about the percentage increases. If you wanted to be clear that despite the extraordinary recovery we are still way below peak vinyl, then you would use the number of records sold.

A repeated argument during the EU referendum was whether the rest of the EU needed UK customers more than UK firms needed the business of the rest of the EU. This was used in arguments about whether or not the UK would get a good trade deal after Brexit.

Prominent Leave supporter Liam Fox talked a great deal about the EU's surplus in trade in goods with the UK – that means that other EU countries sell more of their stuff to the UK than the UK sells to the EU. The UK has a trading surplus in *services* with the EU, but it's not big enough to cancel out the deficit in goods.

Just looking at trade in goods, in 2015 the UK exported £134 billion worth of goods to the rest of the EU and imported £223 billion worth. So, if you were trying to make the argument that the EU needs the UK more then those are the figures that you would use.

On the other hand, in that same year, 47 per cent of the UK's total goods exports went to the rest of the EU, while only 16 per cent of the rest of the EU's exports of goods went to the UK. So if you were trying to argue that the UK needs the EU more then you would use the percentages.

If you heard trade figures being given in cash terms (billions of pounds) you were probably listening to a Leave supporter and if you heard them being referred to as percentages then you were listening to a Remain supporter. Both sets of figures are accurate, but they tell different stories.

While we're looking at the use of percentages in trade figures, Boris Johnson on several occasions described the UK as having been a relatively unsuccessful exporter in the Single Market. He said that in the 20 years after the creation of the Single Market in 1992, 27 other countries that were not in the EU had done better than the UK at exporting to the Single Market. The figure to which he was referring was the percentage increase in the exports of goods to the 11 founding members of the Single Market.

What he was talking about was not which countries had exported the most, it was which countries had achieved the greatest growth in exports. Top of the list was Vietnam, which saw its exports increase from $73 million a month to $400 million a month, a 544 per cent increase. That's impressive growth, but the actual cash amount of exports was still not huge at the end of the period.

The UK, on the other hand, was much lower down the list, having 'only' achieved growth of 81 per cent, but by the end of the period it was exporting $23.9 billion worth of goods per month to the Single Market.

Again, neither figure is inaccurate – it's not wholly unreasonable to define a successful exporter as one that has achieved growth. Indeed, growth seems to be what economists and politicians are most interested in. But without the cash figures as well you're not getting the complete picture. In this case, the UK is doing less well in percentage terms but much better in cash terms.

Percentages are extremely useful for putting figures into context, but if you're being given lonely percentages you should think about why this might be the case.

Another thing to look out for, if a figure does not sound to you like it is reasonably likely to be true, is whether the percentage has been worked out by dividing by the correct number. For example, the former Northern Ireland Secretary Owen Paterson told *BBC Breakfast* in December 2017 that the amount of trade between the UK and the

Republic of Ireland was 'quite small' and used some figures to support that claim. This immediately made me suspicious, because we know that countries being close to each other tends to mean they trade a lot. The Reality Check team looked into the figures that he gave, specifically that 5 per cent of Northern Ireland's exports go to the Republic of Ireland.

Mr Paterson pointed us towards the source of the figure, but it turned out that it was not 5 per cent of Northern Ireland's *exports* that went to the Irish Republic, it was 5 per cent of all goods and services produced in Northern Ireland that were exported to the Republic. He was dividing the amount exported to the Republic by the total amount produced in Northern Ireland, including things consumed in Northern Ireland. That is a strange way to measure exports.

If you work out the proportion of Northern Ireland's actual exports that go to the Republic the figure comes out at 37 per cent, which really cannot be described as 'quite small'. We were pleased to see that Mr Paterson changed his claim before addressing Parliament the following day, when he said 'only 5 per cent of Northern Ireland's sales cross the border south'. That is accurate but looking at exports as a proportion of a figure that includes domestic sales is somewhat unusual, and it was being used to support the claim that the problems of the Northern Ireland border after Brexit were 'easily surmountable'.

The problem in that example was not the figure for sales in the Irish Republic, it was what it was being divided by to come up with a percentage figure. If the percentage you are seeing feels a bit high or a bit low, check what is being divided by what. And while we're talking about confusion over what things are being divided by, just a quick note on another one to look out for.

The employment rate and the unemployment rate do not add up to 100 per cent. The employment rate is the proportion of the total population who are employed. The unemployment rate is the proportion of the economically active population who are unemployed. The difference between the two is the economically inactive part of the population, which is people who are not working and are not available for work or looking for work. I heard somebody on the radio talking about how there is a big gap in the employment rates for men and women of Pakistani origin in the UK because lots of Pakistani women wanted to stay at home and raise their families. This was statistically correct. Later, somebody on the same programme referred back to the research and said there was a gap between the two groups' unemployment rates, which is not accurate. Women staying at home to raise their families do not count as being economically active so they do not appear as part of the unemployment rate.

Another thing to look out for is when a figure hasn't been divided by anything but clearly should have been. I saw a headline on 22 May 2018 asking, 'Where are you most likely to be a victim of crime in Nottingham?' This was a local report (on the Nottinghamshire Live website) of Home Office figures on crimes such as burglaries, robberies and drug offences. The article said that there were 12,357 crimes recorded in the city centre, which makes it the most likely place to become a victim. But this takes no account of how many people live or work in the city centre or pass through it every day. You would expect several times more people to work in the city centre or visit it each day than you would see in a quiet, residential area. It surely can't be a surprise that there are more bicycle thefts in the city centre than there are in other parts of Nottingham. You can't possibly say where you're most likely to be a victim of crime without dividing by some measure of how many people there are in an area.

Percentages are often very useful, but be aware of what the indicator in which you're interested is being divided by to give a percentage rate, and don't be fooled by lonely percentages.

Compound interest and how it can help you understand big percentage changes

Compound interest is just jargon to describe how your savings add up faster if you leave the interest in the account. It's surprisingly important when you're trying to understand big percentage changes in the news.

Let's start with an example to illustrate how it works. To keep the sums easy, imagine you have managed to find a savings account that pays you 10 per cent interest – I know this seems unrealistic (imagine it's the 1990s or you're living in Madagascar or something). You have deposited £100 and you're leaving the money in the account.

Year 1: You get 10 per cent interest, which is £10, taking your total to £110

Year 2: You get 10 per cent of £110, which is £11, taking your total to £121

Year 3: You get 10 per cent of £121, which is £12.10, taking your total to £133.10.

By the end of Year 10 you will have £259.37.

By the end of Year 20 you have £672.75.

So you can see how the amount of interest you are getting each year grows because the amount of money in the account is growing. Over long periods of time the compound interest has a very powerful effect.

The best example of its use is in Douglas Adams's 1980 novel *The Restaurant at the End of the Universe*. The restaurant is enclosed in a vast time bubble and projected forward to the exact moment that the universe ends, allowing guests to eat sumptuous meals while watching all of creation exploding. The interesting element for our purposes is how you pay for it. 'All you have to do is deposit one penny in a savings account in your own era, and when you arrive at the End of Time the operation of compound interest means that the fabulous cost of your meal has been paid for.'

Time travel wreaks havoc with banking systems, but it's a nice idea. If you deposited your penny in a bank account today with a more realistic interest rate of 1 per cent, it would take you more than 200 years to get to 10p, and 463 years to get your first pound. But then it starts speeding up and after 1000 years you would have £209.59, which would be enough for a good meal for two, as long as you're ignoring inflation, which may put a spanner in the works. After 3240 years you would be sitting on £1 trillion. With the universe not expected to end for about six billion years, you can see how the money would add up, although you would have to be sure to pick a really stable economy and a bank with serious staying power.

Compound interest is not just about bank accounts. Oxfam released a report called *Growing a Better Future* in 2011 saying that global food prices would more than double by 2030. When you think about it, food prices operate in the same way as compound interest, because each year's increase comes on top of that of the previous year. The report predicted that food prices would go up by between 120 per cent and 180 per cent. The first thing to say is that that is a huge range, which indicates the massive uncertainty involved in predicting what is going to happen in 20 years. But is it a big number?

An increase of 120 per cent over 20 years is a rise of 4 per cent a year. An increase of 180 per cent over 20 years is 5.3 per cent a year. Is that a lot for global food prices? If you look at the food price index from the United Nations Food and Agriculture Organization (FAO), it turns out that food prices doubled in the ten years before this report was released. So actually, the predicted rises in food prices would have been a considerable slowdown in the rate at which food prices were rising, but that would not have made a terribly good headline. It was a shame in the end that the press release accompanying the report went with the line about food prices doubling, because it seemed to me that there were more important projections in the report. Knowing that prices are rising is not particularly helpful if you do not know what is happening to people's incomes. If everyone has much more money it does not terribly matter that prices are going up. Clearly this is not the case, however, and the more important prediction was that poorer people are going to have to spend a much higher proportion of their money on food than they do at the moment.

Hindsight is a wonderful thing and predicting the future is a mug's game, but if you look at the FAO's food price index now it turns out that 2011 was the peak for global food prices and they have been falling ever since. The index is based on the prices of five key commodity groups: meat, dairy, cereals, vegetable oils and sugar. The falls have been partly due to increased production, which might have been influenced by Oxfam's report, and partly because of the stronger US dollar – commodity prices tend to be listed in dollars so a stronger dollar means more can be bought for the same amount of money. From this we learn that if you can avoid making predictions for the next 20 years it's probably a good idea.

For the purposes of this chapter, the important thing is to understand that doubling over 20 years sounds like a much bigger rise than 4 per cent a year, but compound interest means it is the same thing. Making predictions over decades creates huge uncertainties, but if you understand what a big difference compound interest makes over time then you will be in a better position to understand the forecasts.

In conclusion, don't settle for the percentages and not the absolute figures. I will talk more about why this is important when discussing risk in Chapter 9 – it's very easy to scare people unnecessarily. Remember not to use percentages over 100 per cent because nobody understands what you mean. Hardly anyone gets the difference between percentages and percentage points, but you do now and the distinction is important.

Unlike many people you also now understand that compound interest accelerates your savings because it includes interest paid on the interest earned in previous years. So think about compound interest when you hear about big increases in something over a long period, or when you're trying to save up for a posh meal while the whole of creation explodes around you.

Percentages may be used to mislead people, but it won't work on you now that you know how they work. Oh yes, and the number of goals scored in the Champions League increased by 9.5 per cent between the 2015–16 and 2016–17 seasons.

CHAPTER 5

Averages

Know what you're talking about

The late lamented statistical genius Hans Rosling (1948–2017) pointed out that the average number of legs for people living in Sweden is below two. Nobody has more than two legs and a small number of people have fewer than two, so the average is very slightly below two. What this means is that almost everybody in Sweden (and indeed almost everybody in the world) has an above-average number of legs. The average does not in any way reflect the actual experience of Swedes.

This is an excellent example of an average that has been calculated correctly but is nonetheless unhelpful, because it ignores the way the numbers appear and says nothing about the real people in the data set.

This chapter is about averages and how they can be used to clarify a set of data or muddy the waters around it. We will learn how averages can be useful and representative, but that they are not necessarily an indication of the middle point of a range and may not reveal the whole story. Averages are a way to find a single figure that may tell you something useful about what is going on in the whole data set, but they may also conceal what is happening at the extremes or how much the numbers are spread out. Yet averages are used all the time on the news, generally without being challenged. There are many numbers in this chapter but don't be put off – none of the sums is difficult. This chapter will cover:

• How to work out mean, median and mode

• How you can be misled by the choice of average

• Measures of range

How to work out mean, median and mode

There are three measures of the average that you will come across: the mean, the median and the mode. The mean is what you get if you add up all the numbers and divide by the number of numbers. For example, if you're a cricketer and want to know your average score at the end of the season, you add up the number of runs you scored and divide by the number of times you batted. (Yes, cricket enthusiasts, I know that you need to take into account the number of times you were 'not out', but anyone who has ever seen me bat will know why that is not something that concerns me greatly.) When people refer to an average they are usually talking about the mean.

The median is the middle number. So, if you wanted the median test score in a class of 29 pupils, you would put them in order and take the fifteenth one. If there were 30 pupils you would take a figure half way between the fifteenth and the sixteenth.

The mode is a rarely used but occasionally useful figure – it's the number that appears the most often. If you wanted to know the mode age of professional footballers in France, it would be the age that the largest number of players are. If you took a survey of what method of transport people use to get to work, the mode would be a useful figure as it tells you the method that the largest number of people use.

For another good use of the mode, take a guess at what the average age of death was in England and Wales in 1964. The mean age of death was 65, so that's what you get if you add up the ages of all the people who died that year and divide by the number of people who died. But the mode is the age at which the largest number of people died. And in 1964 that was zero. More people died before their first birthday than at any other age. In 1964 that would have been no great surprise because it had been the case for most years before that. But it has not been the case since, and the fact that we now find it so shocking is a tribute to the extraordinary developments that have been made in healthcare, especially midwifery and neonatal intensive care. In 2016 in the UK, the mode age of death was 86. The mean was 78. And, if you're interested, the median was 81.

Why does this matter? Sometimes you will hear figures referred to as the average and you'll assume it's the mean when actually it's the median. It can make a big difference.

Let's take a look at an example using the ages of the starting team for Arsène Wenger's last home match as manager of Arsenal Football Club, against Burnley in May 2018.

Player	Age
Petr Čech	35
Héctor Bellerín	23
Calum Chambers	23
Konstantinos Mavropanos	20
Sead Kolašinac	24
Alex Iwobi	22
Granit Xhaka	25
Jack Wilshere	26
Henrikh Mkhitaryan	29
Alexandre Lacazette	26
Pierre-Emerick Aubameyang	28

Let's start by working out the mean. If you add up all those ages you get 281. Then you divide that by the number of players, 11, which gives you a mean age of 25 and a half. To work out the median we need to put all the ages in order: 20, 22, 23, 23, 24, 25, 26, 26, 28, 29, 35.

Then we take the middle number – the sixth one – because that is the player for whom half the team are older and half are younger. The median player in this case is Granit Xhaka, who is 25.

And there are two modes, which are 23 and 26 (as there are two players of each of those ages).

The mean and the median are pretty similar, with both of them broadly representative of the sorts of ages appearing in the Arsenal line-up that day.

Now imagine with the score at 5–0, Monsieur Wenger decided that in his 826th Premier League game he was sick of watching from the sideline and was going to bring himself on and show the youngsters how it's done. He warmed up, took his coat off to reveal a pristine red-and-white kit, and told the fourth official to hold up the board to replace the youngest player, Konstantinos Mavropanos.

Arsène was 68 years old, so let's see what he does to our averages. If you add up all the ages you now get 329. If you divide that by 11 you get a touch under 30, which is considerably more than the 25.5 mean we had previously. To find the median we have to write out the ages in order again: 22, 23, 23, 24, 25, 26, 26, 28, 29, 35, 68.

And the middle number – the sixth one – is now 26, one year more than before. The modes haven't changed.

We've added a number that is considerably different to all the others – what statisticians call an outlier. The mean has risen a great deal so that it's now higher than the ages of all but two of the players, but the median has only changed slightly.

And that's the point – you generally use the median if you want to prevent your average being skewed by any outliers.

Let's take another data set to be sure you're getting the hang of this. We'll go with the ages of the celebrity line-up for *Strictly Come Dancing* in 2017. I had great fun with this data set, checking for Reality Check whether it was possible to predict reliably at the halfway point which couples would get to the final. It turned out, not unreasonably, that the number of points the couples had gained so far was a pretty good indicator and that contestants tended to gain marginally fewer points from the samba, rumba, cha-cha-cha and jive. The most interesting thing was that while it looked as if there had been points inflation over the 14 series since the programme was launched, that was in fact a result of the series getting longer, which means the celebrities get more experienced and so were able to pick up higher scores. But the statisticians with whom I was working and I could not find any obvious biases in the system.

Here are the 15 celebrities together with their ages on the day the couples were announced, 9 September 2017.

Dancer	Age
Gemma Atkinson	32
Debbie McGee	58
Chizzy Akudolu	43
Ruth Langsford	57
Aston Merrygold	29
Richard Coles	55
Davood Ghadami	35
Simon Rimmer	54
Charlotte Hawkins	42
Mollie King	30
Alexandra Burke	29
Susan Calman	42
Joe McFadden	41
Jonnie Peacock	24
Brian Conley	56

Let's start with the mean. If you add up all the ages you get 627. If you divide them by the number of dancers – 15 – you get 41.8.

To work out the median you need to put the ages in order and take the middle one. The ages in order are: 24, 29, 29, 30, 32, 35, 41, 42, 42, 43, 54, 55, 56, 57, 58.

We need the eighth number, which is 42, so the mean and median are pretty close to each other. There are two modes, which are 29 and 42.

Now imagine that the world's oldest person was added to the line-up for *Strictly*. They are certainly a celebrity, but you would be surprised if they got very far in the show. Naming the world's oldest age-verified person at the time of writing would be fool-hardy, so let's just take their age as 117. Now if you add up all the ages you get 744. If you divide that by the new number of contestants – 16 – you get the mean figure, which is 46.5.

To get the median you put the new age at the end of the above list of ages in order, and instead of taking the eighth figure you take a number halfway between the eighth and the ninth. In this case that doesn't make any difference and the median remains 42. There's also no change to the modes.

The introduction of a massive outlier in this case increases the mean by 4.7 years, but the median and mode remain unchanged. Once again, the mean has been shifted a long way by the outlier – 10 of the 16 contestants are now below the mean age. But the median has been unaffected.

In these examples we see how the choice of averages may influence how much your figures are affected by outliers. None of them is necessarily wrong as long as you have explained what you're doing, but you need to know which has been chosen, because there are great dangers of being misled.

How you can be misled by the choice of average

Now you know how to calculate the mean, median and mode, and we've started thinking about why you might choose one instead of another, we can start to look at some of the dangers of averages. How you choose to measure the average can completely change the impression given by a set of figures. Here are some of the potential pitfalls.

In the example at the start of the chapter, the mean was clearly the wrong sort of average to choose when trying to say something about how many legs people in Sweden have. The median and even the mode would have been better choices.

The choice of averages really does make a big difference. The Office for National Statistics works out average earnings across the economy every month based on the mean. For 2017 it was running at an average of about £500 a week. But the ONS also produces the Annual Survey of Hours and Earnings (ASHE), which has a figure for average weekly earnings calculated using the median, and for 2017 that came out at about £450 a week. Where has that £50 a week difference come from? It is almost certainly the case that a relatively small number of very high earners has skewed weekly pay across the whole economy by that much – it's about 10 per cent.

It's when you are looking at earnings that the differences between the different averages are particularly important. Consider the difference that Arsène Wenger made to the average age of the Arsenal team and now imagine how much difference it would make to average earnings if you had ten normal earners in the room and Bill Gates walked in.

Remember the package of tax cuts introduced in the USA by Donald Trump in 2017? The non-partisan Tax Policy Center calculated that taxes would be reduced by $1600 on average in 2018, increasing taxpayers' income after tax by 2.2 per cent on average.

Is that a helpful figure? It's going to look pretty inflated if you are one of the poorest 20 per cent of Americans, who will on average get a tax cut of $60, which is 0.4 per cent of their income after tax, or the next 20 per cent up who will get $380 or 1.2 per cent. In fact, the only group that sees an increase in its income of 2.2 per cent or more is the richest 20 per cent, whose average income rises by 2.9 per cent, which is worth an average $7640. The research found that 65 per cent of the benefit from the federal tax cuts would go to the richest 20 per cent.

While the average overall cut may be accurate, the vast majority of taxpayers will benefit much less, both in cash terms and as a percentage of their incomes. To see why that is, you need look no further than the benefit to the top 1 per cent of taxpayers who gain an average tax cut of 3.4 per cent, worth an average $51,140. The very large gains by the highest income Americans skew the average for taxpayers as a whole so much that at least 80 per cent of taxpayers are in income groups that can expect to see a smaller-than-average cut as a proportion of their income.

Income inequality means this is always something you need to look out for when you are considering averages across income groups. Relatively small numbers of big earners distort these sorts of figures a great deal if you're only using the mean. If there is no attempt made to explain how the money is distributed beyond a single figure then you probably aren't getting the full picture.

Another area where you may have seen different types of averages being used recently is in the figures for the gender pay gap. The first thing to remember is that whether a company has a gender pay gap and whether it has equal pay are not the same thing. The gender pay gap is the difference between the average amount men are paid per hour and the average amount women are paid. It takes no account of whether the men and women in the company are doing different jobs. Equal pay is about making sure that people doing the same or similar jobs are paid the same – it's a legal requirement. There are no reliable figures for how many companies are not offering equal pay because it is illegal. We have no idea what's happened to equal pay claims in employment tribunals because, since 2011, of the many thousands of equal pay claims that went to tribunals, 0 per cent were officially listed as successful at a hearing and 0 per cent were officially listed as unsuccessful at hearing. I'm assured by employment lawyers that this is because, on the whole, as soon as the legal points have been decided, the parties tend to settle the matter between themselves, but this is hardly justice being done in public, and does nothing to help our understanding of the scale of the problem.

Having a big gender pay gap does not necessarily mean that pay is unequal, but it may say something about hiring practices. A company running a chain of pre-schools, for example, would be much more likely to have women working in the nurseries than men, because almost all nursery teachers are women. That means that any men working in the business would be relatively more likely to work in management than looking after small children. This company may well have a big gender pay gap, despite offering equal pay to people doing the same job. On the other hand, a company with no gender pay gap could still be failing to offer equal pay. Imagine a company with four employees: a male and a female salesperson and a male and female manager. If the male salesperson was being paid a bit less than the female one and the male manager was being paid a bit more than his female colleague, there would be no gender pay gap but, all other things being equal, there might well be a case for unequal pay.

In the UK, companies employing 250 people or more have to tell the government their gender pay gaps, measured both by the mean and by the median. To get the mean gender pay gap you work out the mean average pay for the men in an organisation and for the women, and report the difference. It's the same with the median. Having both figures is useful – if your organisation has a much bigger mean pay gap than median pay gap it probably means that there are outliers, generally a small number of men being paid a lot.

But there are other tricky things to bear in mind when you are looking at gender pay gap statistics, in particular whether the figures are only for full-time employees or for all employees. The figures are reported as average pay per hour, so they would not be skewed by some people working more hours per week. The problem is that part-time work tends to be less well paid per hour and women are much more likely to do it. If you are trying to make your gender pay gap look smaller you might consider reporting only the gap for full-time staff.

It's these sorts of differences that meant that *Spectator* editor Fraser Nelson was able to say that, for women born after 1975, there is no gender pay gap – that's because he was only looking at full-time workers. If you're only looking at female workers, part-time workers get paid about a third less than full-time workers. And as women are much more likely to work part time, it means much of the gender pay gap is actually a part-time, full-time pay gap. Also, although there is still a gender pay gap, the situation has been improving, so only looking at women born after 1975 makes the figures look as good as possible.

If you were trying to make your gender pay gap look smaller you could also consider outsourcing some of the lower-paid functions in your company such as cleaning or call centres or catering. If you have more low-paid women doing these sorts of jobs, getting another company in to do them will remove them from your gender pay gap figures. The same would work if you were trying to reduce the amount more than the rest of the staff that the chief executive is being paid – outsource all the lower-paid functions in your company and suddenly your management is being paid a smaller multiple of the average salary.

When you're looking at these sorts of averages,

notice whether the organisation is using the mean or the median and check who is being included or excluded from the data. Also, think about what the data you are being told about is likely to look like. If you think there are going to be lots of extreme cases such as very rich people or very old people, you might question whether the average you are being given is really representative of the data set.

Measures of range

Michael Blastland and Andrew Dilnot's excellent book *The Tiger That Isn't* (2007) gives a great example of why averages may be misleading. A drunk swaying down the street between the two pavements will on average be walking in a straight line along the white lines. The traffic going in both directions will, on average, be able to avoid him. 'On average, he stays alive. In fact, he walks under a bus.'

If you're looking for somewhere to live with a comfortable climate you probably shouldn't look at the average temperature because you might end up in a desert that is very hot during the day and very cold at night, or somewhere that is extremely hot in summer and covered in snow all winter.

The problem with averages is that a single number may make it look as if everything is smooth and simple, when in fact that may not be the case. You would get the same average path for the drunk whether he or she was swaying between pavements or walking in a straight line. That's why in addition to being given the average figure, you may also be given a figure for the spread, or the range, or the deviation. Here's how it works.

There are various measures available for the spread of your data. In the case of the weather example, the simplest measure of the range would be to take just the maximum temperature and the minimum temperature. That would help if you were interested in avoiding extremes, but it would be less useful if, for example, you were looking at a place where the temperature was pretty much the same every day but there was one really hot day and one really cold day every year.

A better measure of spread, and one that you will see more often, is the standard deviation. The standard deviation is a measure of how far the figures are spread away from the mean – the lower the standard deviation the smaller the spread. If you were looking at the ages of a school football team taken from a single year group, the standard deviation would be close to zero.

Instead, let's work out the standard deviation for the ages of that Arsenal team against Burnley.

The first thing you need to do in order to work out the standard deviation is calculate how far away from the mean is each figure in your data set. Remember, the mean was 25.5, so we want to know how far each figure is away from 25.5.

Player	Age	Deviation from mean
Petr Čech	35	9.5
Héctor Bellerín	23	-2.5
Calum Chambers	23	-2.5
Konstantinos Mavropanos	20	-5.5
Sead Kolašinac	24	-1.5
Alex Iwobi	22	-3.5
Granit Xhaka	25	-0.5
Jack Wilshere	26	0.5
Henrikh Mkhitaryan	29	3.5
Alexandre Lacazette	26	0.5
Pierre-Emerick Aubameyang	28	2.5

There's no point taking an average of those deviations because that would give you zero. (It actually gives us a little more than that here because we've rounded the mean down to 25.5, but it's close enough.) Instead, we square all those deviations, so that the average will not be zero – we will take a square root later so it all works out. Squaring them has the advantage that all the figures we end up with are positive, which is good because we are interested in how far the figures are from the mean, not whether they are positive or negative.

Deviation	Squared
9.5	90.25
-2.5	6.25
-2.5	6.25
-5.5	30.25
-1.5	2.25
-3.5	12.25
-0.5	0.25
0.5	0.25
3.5	12.25
0.5	0.25
2.5	6.25

Now we take the mean of all those squares. They add up to 167. If you divide that by 11 you get a mean of 15.2. Finally, we take a square root of that number (because we squared them all earlier) and you get 3.9. That means the mean age of the team was 25.5 with a standard deviation of 3.9.

Now let's see what happens to the standard deviation after 68-year-old Arsène Wenger brings himself on in place of Mavropanos. If you want to work this one out by yourself now, grab a piece of paper. The answer will be at the end of the chapter.

While you're thinking about that one, let's sum up what we've learned. Averages are used to summarise a set of data at a glance, which is useful but sometimes dangerous. The mean, median and mode are each suitable for certain circumstances and misleading for others, and knowing which one is being used and why is crucial. A measure of how spread out the numbers are is also very helpful.

As a shortcut for situations when you may need to dig a little further into the figures, look out for qualifications such as the ones in the gender pay-gap example, when the average only covered full-time workers and those born since 1975.

A single figure to sum up a data set may be helpful, but it may also be misleading, and now you have the tools to spot which it is.

Now back to Mr Wenger's somewhat unorthodox substitution. With the manager playing on the team, the mean has risen to just under 30 and the standard deviation is 12.5, which is a big standard deviation, showing how spread out these figures are.

Just to illustrate the point further, we could go back to the starting team and replace the goalkeeper, who is himself an outlier in terms of age, with the substitute keeper David Ospina, who is 29. That would take the mean age down to 25 and the standard deviation to just 2.8.

CHAPTER 6

Big Numbers
Understanding billions, trillions and quadrillions

I was chatting with my 12-year-old son Isaac over breakfast on Budget Day. The children know it's Budget Day because I wear a hat, which says 'Hooray, it's Budget Day' that I had made specially. My wife tries to avoid being seen with me that day. There has been much discussion about what hat I should commission for other fiscal events: kudos to my colleague who suggested I should get one saying 'Public sector pay cap' and then I could raise it when necessary.

I was explaining to Isaac that Budget Day is when we find out how the government is going to be spending all the money. 'How much is the budget?' he asked me.

'About £850 million,' I sleepily told him.

'That doesn't sound like very much,' he said.

And of course, when I woke myself up and

thought about it, he was right. The government actually spends about £850 *billion* a year. He hasn't let me forget it since.

In this chapter I am going to talk about the challenges caused by big numbers. Really big numbers. Numbers so big it looks like somebody has fallen asleep with their nose resting on the zero key. Big numbers are difficult to deal with because our brains are not very well tuned to them. We can cope with small numbers because we have experienced them. You know what a group of ten people would look like and you could probably manage to visualise a crowd of a hundred. If you have been to a football game you might be able to cope with what 30,000 or even 100,000 people look like. If you have tried to buy a house you may have experience of hundreds of thousands, but there's very little in life that prepares us for dealing with billions or trillions. The very idea that £850 million could not be much money is one with which most of us struggle, even when properly awake. It's a growing challenge. When I first started working in business news in 1995, the total output of the UK economy was under £750 billion a year and that was about the biggest number with which I'd have to deal. The news contained millions and the occasional billion. Now, with the output of the economy approaching £2 trillion, there are more and more numbers in the news that sound big but are not. The government can announce that it's going to spend many millions of pounds on something, but in context that will be just a drop in the ocean. The classic example of this, cited in *The Tiger That Isn't*, was the pledge in the early years of Tony Blair's government to spend £300 million over five years to provide one million childcare places. So that's £300 per place, or £60 per place per year, which is not enough money for the policy.

There are three key techniques for making sure you're not being misled in this area:

- Double-check whether you mean millions, billions or quadrillions

- Put big numbers into context

- Remember a few key figures to help you understand big numbers

Double-check whether you mean millions, billions or quadrillions

Returning to my error over breakfast on Budget Day, I had made one of the most common errors in big numbers – saying millions when I meant billions. This will only become more of a problem as we report lots of trillions and even the occasional quadrillion.

A million is a one followed by 6 zeroes, a billion has 9 zeroes, a trillion has 12 zeroes and a quadrillion has 15 zeroes. If you have a nagging feeling that there is some difference between a British billion and a US billion, you used to be right. A British billion used to be a million million – that's 12 zeroes – while a US billion has 9 zeroes. Can you imagine the confusion that must have caused? In 1974, Robin Maxwell-Hyslop, MP for Tiverton, asked a written question of Prime Minister Harold Wilson, requesting that his ministers should agree only to use the British billion instead of the US version. The Prime Minister replied that a thousand million being a billion was now the internationally accepted version and his ministers would be using that. From that point, the British billion was abandoned and everywhere in the English-speaking world a billion is one followed by nine zeroes.

While I am confessing to my big number errors, I was once on *PM* on Radio 4 being interviewed by Eddie Mair, who has sadly now left the BBC. I was talking about trillions of things and he asked me how many zeroes that was. On the whole, live broadcasting does not make me particularly nervous, but suddenly at that moment I understood what happens to contestants on game shows under the studio lights when they give dumb answers to simple questions and we all throw stuff at the telly. I am eternally ashamed to say that I told him it was nine. He asked me another question – I started answering but my mind was elsewhere, and halfway through a sentence I stopped and said, 'No, hang on, a trillion is twelve zeroes.' The point is that anyone can make this mistake, so it's a good place to start when you're wondering if something is likely to be true.

Talking of mistakes, the first time I came across a quadrillion on the BBC News website was in October 2012 in a story about a woman in France who received a phone bill of just under 12 quadrillion euros. The exact figure was 11,721,000,000,000,000 euros. She phoned up her provider and suggested they might have made a mistake. They said it was definitely correct and offered to let her pay in instalments. In the piece, it was explained that even if she had paid in instalments equal to the entire output of the French economy it would still take her 6000 years to pay the bill. Now that's a big number. The phone company later admitted that it had made a mistake, said the bill should have been 117.21 euros, and waived it altogether, so there was a happy ending.

My only problem with the story was that it used 'qn' in the headline as an abbreviation for quadrillion. I know we use 'bn' for billion and 'tn' for trillion, but if you're going to use 'qn' for quadrillion it leaves you nowhere to go when we start reporting quintillions – that's a one with 18 zeroes. And indeed, we have had quintillions in the news. In 2014, when Psy's hit 'Gangnam Style' threatened to exceed the maximum number that the YouTube counters could cope with (just over two billion) the website updated its systems so that they could count up to 9.2 quintillion. I had thought that was the highest number ever reported by the BBC until a reader corrected me, pointing to a story from 2011 about a new system for allocating internet addresses, which created 340 undecillion possible addresses. An undecillion is a one followed by 36 zeroes, in case you weren't sure.

While these numbers may sound made up, they are not, unlike a zillion or a bajillion. But I often think that there is a place for made-up big numbers. They have been championed by US academic Stephen Chrisomalis, who calls them indefinite hyperbolic numbers. If we want to talk about, for example, single-use plastic straws, we know that loads of them are used each year, but we don't have a reliable estimate. So instead of coming up with an unreliable estimate that can be challenged, perhaps distracting people from the problem, we could say there are a squillion of them being used – it's a big number but we don't know what it is. This works well in conversation – 'I've told you umpteen times' is another good example. I'm not sure we're ready for it in more formal settings yet. 'The head of the NHS announced today that he would need an extra jillion pounds of funding over the next 10 years,' might sound a bit odd in the news headlines. It would certainly take some getting used to.

It is interesting, however, that there is a clear ranking of the size of these numbers, with umpteen being a relatively small non-specific number, a zillion or jillion certainly being more than a million, but not as much as a gazillion or bajillion, with the prefixes ga- or ba- increasing the perceived size of the number.

Put big numbers into context

To deal with genuine enormous numbers as opposed to made-up ones, you need some context, just as the French phone bill story used the economic output of France to get across what a ludicrously big number it was.

If your head is spinning with the size of all these numbers then you're not alone. My favourite attempt at helping came in a video called 'Obama Budget Cuts Visualization' on YouTube. It followed an announcement from President Obama that he was going to cut $100 million from the Federal Budget. We already know from my son that $100 million is not a lot of money when you're talking about a national budget, but maybe it's breakfast time and you need a bit of help with numbers this big. The video points out that taking $100 million out of a

$3.5 trillion budget sounds to the listener like taking a big pile of money out of a bigger pile of money. This is the key to the problem – when the numbers are this big we just can't visualise the difference between them. So, our filmmaker goes to the bank and gets 8880 one-cent pieces and puts them on his table in piles of five, each of which represents $2 billion – so each coin is $400 million. He picks up one of the pennies and cuts it in half with a pair of pliers. Then he takes one of the halves and cuts that in half again to get a quarter. He returns three quarters of the penny to the table and explains that President Obama plans to find a way to cut the remaining quarter of a penny from a Federal Budget represented by 8880 pennies. It's interesting that this visual explanation helps when other attempts have failed. The financial crisis was a terrible time for having to deal with big numbers – the figures involved were ludicrous. Sometimes, people would try to explain the bailout in terms of how much the money would weigh in £10 notes or how many times it would get to the moon if you stacked pound coins on top of each other. I think that was just replacing incomprehensibly big numbers with incomprehensibly big weights or distances.

The EU referendum campaign in 2016 threw up lots of interesting and contentious statistics, but one above all others has become notorious and is the enduring image of the campaign. I am talking, of course, about the £350-million bus. The Vote Leave campaign wrote on the side of its campaign bus: 'We send the EU £350m a week – let's fund our NHS instead'. The problem with it was that we did not send that amount of money as our contribution to the EU Budget because the rebate was deducted before any money was sent. The rebate is a discount that the UK gets on its contributions to the EU Budget – it was originally negotiated by Margaret Thatcher in 1984. BBC Reality Check pointed out the problem with the figure when it was being used in interviews, long before it appeared on the bus. Later, the UK Statistics Authority (UKSA), which is the UK's independent statistics regulator, ruled that it was potentially misleading, so any further discussion was just arguing with the referee, which is pointless. The UKSA was particularly worried about the idea that the £350 million could all be spent on the NHS, because part of it is the rebate, so is not spent at all, and parts of it are spent by the EU on things in the UK such as supporting farmers, scientific research and regional aid, all of which would leave people cross if they thought their funding was being diverted to the NHS. Even the most enthusiastic users of the figure now refer to the £350 million as the amount of money over which the UK loses control, rather than the amount the UK sends to Brussels. The £350 million was not in itself a misleading statistic – it is the correct figure for the UK's contribution to the EU Budget before the rebate is taken off, but that's not how it was described on the bus.

The £350 million presented two separate big-number problems. The first one was that the correct figure for the amount that the UK was sending to the EU each week was £276 million. Clearly there is a difference between £276 million and £350 million – it's about 25 per cent – but to anyone listening it was just two big piles of money. And every time somebody argued that the bus should say £276 million instead of £350 million, it still highlighted the fact that the UK was contributing a big pile of money to the EU Budget.

The second big-number problem was the context in which £350 million, or indeed £276 million, was not really a lot of money at all. The Institute for Fiscal Studies and the International Monetary Fund both pointed out that the UK's contribution to the EU Budget would be completely dwarfed by any impact on the economy as a whole. The output of the UK economy is about £2 trillion a year. If Brexit means that the economy grows by 1 per cent a year more than it would have done, or by 1 per cent less, the difference it would make to government finances would be more than the contribution to the EU Budget.

We have seen how figures can be used to put other figures into context, making big numbers more manageable and easier to understand. But not all numbers would work with this. If you divided the size of the US Federal Budget by the number of cats in the USA, you would get a smaller number expressed in terms of spending per cat, but that wouldn't be very helpful.

The question is, which numbers do you use to put figures into context, and that depends very much on the sort of number with which you're dealing. If you're talking about funding for education it may be worth dividing by the number of pupils or the number of schools. In the example at the start of the book, dividing the number of plastic straws used per year by the population meant you could immediately take a view on whether the figure is likely to be true. If you can personalise the number and relate it to something you can comprehend then you will probably find it easier to cope with.

For a large sum of money, a good option is to compare it with areas of government spending. Once you start talking about amounts of money at national budget levels, there are always going to be big-number problems. And it's not just whole government spending that creates these difficulties – the National Health Service is so big that it's hard to talk about anything to do with it without losing people in the numbers. The budget for NHS England is about £115 billion a year, which is an unimaginably large amount of money. I suggested at the 2015 general election that we should get round the big-number problem by doing what physicists do. A light year is the distance that light travels in a year, which is about 5.9 trillion miles or 9.5 trillion kilometres. That means you can express mind-bogglingly big distances as just a small number of light years, making it easier to cope. If we take an NHS yearly budget as £115 billion then other large amounts of money could be expressed in terms of how long they would fund the NHS. An NHS month would be just under £10 billion and an NHS week would be just over £2 billion. The £350 million on the bus would have been a touch more than an NHS day. The slight problem with the NHS year as the yardstick for large amounts of money is that it is not a constant – it changes from year to year, whereas a light year is always the same distance. On the other hand, that means it incorporates a measure of inflation, which may be useful when considering large amounts of money. In other words, as things get more expensive across the economy, so too does an NHS year.

The NHS is also a big employer with about 1.5 million workers, which makes it the world's fifth biggest employer behind the US Department of Defence, the Chinese army, Walmart and McDonald's. Such scale makes some news about the NHS a bit difficult to assess. Take the time an anti-cuts campaign group released the shock news that the NHS was planning to cut 53,000 jobs. If you read in a bit further it turned out that the group had put in freedom of information requests to calculate the number, which was spread over the next five years. I'm not taking a view on how much the NHS would be poorer for having 53,000 fewer staff, or indeed the damage that would be caused to those households by the loss of employment. My problem with the analysis was that I didn't believe it was accurate enough to be correct to within 10,600 jobs a year out of a total of 1.5 million. So 53,000 jobs sounds like a lot, but that's because all headlines about the NHS sound like a lot, be they reports of unfilled posts, extra funding or budget deficits. Try to think about such reports in the context of what an extraordinary institution the NHS is.

Another useful example came from a headline in the *Daily Mail* on 2 September 2009: 'Town hall bans staff from using Facebook after they waste 572 hours in ONE month' (that's the *Mail*'s capitalisation). It turned out the story was about Portsmouth City Council, which was blocking access to Facebook for its 4500 staff. What are you going to divide by to establish whether this is a big number? Start by converting 572 hours into minutes to make the sums easier – it's 34,320. Then divide that by the 4500 staff to get 7.6 minutes. And that's 7.6 minutes a month spent on social media by each member of staff – if you divide again by the 21 working days in a month you get to about 22 seconds a day per employee, which really isn't a big number. Later in the story, it turns out that some members of staff are supposed to be using social media to check up on the lifestyles of benefits claimants. So really the headline should have been: 'Town hall massively overreacts to tiny use of social media by staff'. That's also a good story, perhaps even a better story than the original. It illustrates another point, which is that numbers in headlines are enormously powerful. Almost everybody reading that article would have come away thinking that Portsmouth City Council employees were wasting huge amounts of taxpayer-funded time posting things on Facebook, which just wasn't true, but there is no question that is what the *Mail* wanted you to believe.

Although context is important when you're dealing with big numbers, some people get upset about the ways that big numbers are put into context.

When I first started as the BBC's head of statistics I went to give a talk at the Office for National Statistics. At the end, I asked the audience what annoyed them most about numbers in the news. One of the delegates asked me if I could persuade the BBC to stop referring to areas as multiples of the size of Wales (the ONS headquarters is in Newport). I said I couldn't do that because coping with big numbers in the news relies on things being the size of Wales, the volume of an Olympic-sized swimming pool, enough to fill Wembley Stadium, the length of a jumbo jet or the height of a number of double-decker buses.

Clearly there are problems with this. I objected to the reporting of a chimney due for demolition as being the height of 55 double-decker buses stacked on top of each other on the grounds that if you stacked that many buses on top of each other the bottom ones would get squashed. It was much more sensible to describe it as more than double the height of Big Ben (or the tower containing Big Ben, although that doesn't trip off the tongue in the same way). I suspect people have little idea how big Wales is, but saying something is the size of Wales probably means more to them than saying it's just over 8000 square miles or almost 21,000 square kilometres.

I have also seen people try to use the size of an elephant as a standard measure for something big. I received research suggesting that the amount of reusable rubbish being sent to landfill weighed the same as 90,000 elephants. That feels like it's just using one big number to replace another and not really helping with the context at all, not to mention the fact that there is a big range in the size of elephants. Perhaps they would have been better off using the weight of Wembley Stadium or indeed the weight of whales – or even Wales.

The cash comparison that I find unhelpful is comparing people's salaries to that of the Prime

Minister. We're always hearing how the chief executives of some councils or NHS trusts are paid more than the PM. The PM's salary is kept artificially low for political reasons, at about £150,000, but that doesn't include the rent-free residences that come with the job: 10 Downing Street and Chequers. The use of an attractive Central London residence and a mansion in the country must be worth a fair bit.

Similarly, you often hear rich people or valuable companies being described as worth more than particular countries. This is a bogus comparison because the value of the country is almost always measured by its gross domestic product or GDP, which is the amount its economy produces in a year. That is then compared with the total wealth of an individual or the market capitalisation (the value of all the shares put together) of the company. Clearly this is not comparing like with like. If you compared an individual's salary or a company's sales for a year with a country's GDP it might make more sense, although it's still not terribly illuminating.

We have seen how dividing a giant phone bill by the economic output of France or the amount of time spent on social media by the number of staff in a town hall has helped with our understanding of big numbers, while dividing the US Federal Budget into 8880 on YouTube demonstrated how $100 million wasn't really a big number. It's not tricky maths – it's just using division to provide the context that helps you understand whether or not you should be getting excited about particular numbers.

Remember a few key figures to help you understand big numbers

It's useful to have a few key figures at your fingertips to help you understand big numbers. It's fine if these are rounded up or down because the bar is set at the level of 'reasonably likely to be true'. I'm as bad as anybody at remembering or estimating some of these. The ONS put together a quiz in which you had to say how many people lived in your local area and how many of them had jobs or university degrees, for example. I was terrible at it. I suspect most people were. The pollsters Ipsos Mori carry out an annual poll in 40 countries called 'The Perils of Perception', in which it turns out that we have very little idea about things such as what proportion of the population come from ethnic minorities, what proportion are homeowners and how much the country spends on healthcare.

Here are ten statistics about the UK, rounded to make them easier to remember (or perhaps you could bookmark this page if you can't remember them). These figures are all from the ONS.

- UK population is about 65 million – 55 million in England, 5 million in Scotland, 3 million in Wales and 2 million in Northern Ireland; almost 9 million live in London.

- About half of those people are employed; about three-quarters of those aged 16 to 64 are employed.

- There are about three-quarters of a million live births in the UK a year and 600,000 deaths.

- The total output of the UK economy measured by GDP is about £2 trillion a year.

- According to the 2011 Census, 86 per cent of the population of England and Wales is white; the next biggest group is Asian/Asian British at 7.5 per cent followed by Black/African/Caribbean/ Black British at 3.3 per cent.

- 59 per cent of the population of England and Wales identify as Christian, 25 per cent have no religion and 5 per cent are Muslims; the Census question was optional and 7 per cent didn't answer.

- Just over nine million of the UK population were not born in the UK while about six million are not UK nationals.

- About 65 per cent of UK households are owner-occupiers, 17 per cent rent from a private land-lord and 18 per cent from a social landlord.

- The average (median) weekly wage for a full-time employee in the UK is £550; that's £28,600 a year.

- The UK's national debt is about £1.7 trillion.

Challenging big numbers is all about confidence. If you have a few carefully chosen numbers at your fingertips, you can use them to put the figures you hear into context. Also, you can be pretty sure that your friends and family don't know the ten indicators above off the top of their heads, so it's a great opportunity to get ahead in arguments.

Do bear in mind that everybody confuses millions and billions occasionally so you always need to double-check. When you see a figure in a headline that looks big, stop to think about whether it really is, especially if it involves government spending or debt, which always throw up huge sums.

You're now ready to deal with big numbers.

CHAPTER 7

Correlation and Causation

Did this really cause that?

I heard a frustrating interview on the radio, introduced by the newsline: 'People admitted to hospital with a head injury are twice as likely to die over the next 13 years as people who haven't suffered that kind of injury.'

There was then an interview with the chap from the University of Glasgow who had led the research. We learned from him that the people who had suffered the head injuries were dying of just the same things as the rest of the population and it was 'not entirely clear' why their death rate was higher. They had tried adjusting for gender, age and social deprivation, but that didn't explain away the effect.

The professor said he was now going to do some more research and find out if there were other lifestyle factors involved (in other words, are people who end up in hospital with head injuries more likely to do things that get themselves killed within the next 13 years?) or whether there is some other 'underlying biological cause'.

The possibility that was not mentioned was that this was all just a coincidence.

This chapter is about correlation – two things are correlated if one goes up or down at the same time as the other. It does not mean that they have anything to do with each other. We hear all the time in the news about how eating particular things makes us more or less likely to get cancer, for example. It's really hard to prove that one thing is causing another and it is certainly not safe to assume it is just because both have gone up at the same time.

Correlations are very useful if you are looking for things to investigate, but they can create problems in the news when they are used without further evidence to suggest that one thing is causing another.

In this chapter we will look at the three questions to ask when you assess things that are correlated:

• Is this a coincidence?

• What else is going on?

• Are the numbers oddly specific?

Is this a coincidence?

Modern spreadsheets are so powerful that you can put pretty much anything going on along one axis and pretty much everything else along the other and find out if anything correlates to anything else. Remember, a correlation is when one thing goes up or down at the same time as another thing goes up or down. It doesn't mean that one thing is causing the other.

This is beautifully demonstrated by a website called Spurious Correlations, which plots charts showing correlations between things such as the amount of cheese eaten per person in the USA and the number of people killed by becoming tangled in their bedsheets. There was also a clear correlation between the number of people who drowned after falling into a pool each year with the number of films Nicolas Cage appeared in.

In *The Tiger That Isn't*, Michael Blastland and Andrew Dilnot give the example of somebody throwing a bowl of rice in the air. When the rice ends up on the ground, there are some places with little piles of rice and there are other areas where there is no rice at all. And we all just understand that this is the way it is with rice falling on the ground. But when we are talking about things that sound like they might be linked, such as people dying in the years after they have suffered a head injury or unusually large numbers of people in an area getting a particular type of cancer, our brains are attuned to looking for patterns, and the explanation that this is all just a coincidence is desperately unsatisfying. Blastland and Dilnot offer the explanation that this is a survival instinct – it's better to be safe than sorry when deciding whether the pattern in the trees is just an illusion caused by light and shifting leaves or a real tiger – hence the title of their book. It's hard to fight the urge to find patterns and things causing other things when we see sets of numbers, but we need to try if we are going to avoid being misled. This is all metaphorical, incidentally. If there's a chance there might be a real tiger involved then my advice is to be on the safe side and run for it.

When the radio presenter said that the head-injury case was 'quite an alarming finding', she was right, but it shouldn't have been. It's certainly an interesting finding, and a good basis for applying for research funding to investigate whether there is something going on, but until there is any reason to believe that it's not a coincidence it shouldn't really be getting out to an audience that could be unnecessarily alarmed. After all, it's not as if people will be going around trying to get head injuries if they don't think it will increase their chances of dying of something else in the following years.

Demonstrating that two things that correlate are also causing each other is very hard. In health research, the way to show something causes something else is with a randomised controlled trial (RCT). In a classic RCT you get a bunch of people and randomly allocate them into two groups, one of which is given the treatment you are testing and one of which is given a placebo (something like a tablet with no active ingredient), and neither group knows who is getting the new treatment. Because the allocation is random, there is a decent chance that any differences in the outcome for members of the groups will be due to the treatment you are testing.

Now consider how you would run an RCT to show that being admitted to hospital with a head injury caused people to double their chances of death in the following 13 years. You would take a group of people and divide them randomly into two groups. Then you would beat all the members of one group about the head hard enough for them to need to be admitted to hospital. After that, you would wait 13 years to see how many members of each group had died. It would be tricky to get this piece of research past the ethics committee, which is why people try to use other statistical methods.

So, to confirm, it is very difficult to demonstrate that one thing is causing another without either using an RCT or finding the mechanism by which it happens.

The great exception that proves this rule is smoking. It is now generally accepted that smoking causes cancer, although there have been no RCTs, because the weight of evidence is so overwhelming even without a full understanding of the mechanism. Again, you would struggle to run an RCT on smoking because you would have to find a group of people and randomly choose half of them to start smoking and the other half not to, and then observe who got cancer in the following years. The causal link being accepted between smoking and cancer is unusual.

Another big advantage of RCTs is that you decide in advance what you're looking for, making the outcome much less likely to be a coincidence. Well-designed experiments also mean you can't just do the test over and over again until you get a significant result. As a simple example of this, it's very unlikely that you will flip a coin ten times in a row and get heads each time – the odds are about one in 1000. The illusionist Derren Brown once did this on television using a single continuous camera shot, but he later explained that the footage that was broadcast was just the last minute of nine hours of filming him failing to get ten heads in a row. It was in a programme called *The System* (2008) in which he managed to send five consecutive correct predictions about which horses would win a series of races. It turned out that the way he had done it was to take a group of thousands of people, divide it into six and send the name of one of the six horses in a particular race to each group. Then in the next round he would take the group of people who had been sent the winner of the previous race, divide that up into six and so on until the only person left was one woman who had received five consecutive correct predictions. The woman, of course, believed that Derren had the unfaltering ability to predict the outcome of any race. It was an extraordinary lesson in how we can be led by our own perceptions and how badly we can be misled. He used it to make a point about things such as homeopathic remedies. If we take something when we're feeling unwell and we end up feeling a bit better, we will be absolutely convinced it is what we have taken that has made us feel better regardless of whether tests on thousands of people have found them to be ineffective. We have taken something at the same time as we have started feeling better so we assume that one thing has caused the other.

In his 1954 classic *How to Lie with Statistics*, Darrell Huff talks about the use of vaccines and antihistamines as cures for the common cold. As a cold will eventually cure itself, given time, you can give people any sort of treatment you like and be reasonably confident that they will feel better within a week or so. You can then give the credit to whatever treatment you have recommended and many people will be convinced – personal experience is extremely powerful.

When it comes to designing research experiments, as well as planning the experiment in advance it is also good to have a hypothesis that you are testing. Some newspapers and magazines were taken in by a hoax piece of research, conducted in 2015 by a journalist called John Bohannon, which fooled them into reporting that eating chocolate accelerated weight loss. Fifteen volunteers were recruited and divided into three groups – one group was put onto a low-carbohydrate diet, one was put on the same diet but told to eat a 1.5oz bar of dark chocolate every day and the third group, the control group, was told to carry on eating as usual. At the end, the control group had not lost any weight at all. The two groups on diets lost an average of five pounds in three weeks, but the group eating the dark chocolate lost the weight a bit faster.

This sounds like a well-designed study and it was published in a journal and in some newspapers. What was not included in the reports was the fact that the study examined 18 different measurements such as weight, cholesterol, blood protein levels and quality of sleep. In a study of only 15 people there was likely to be a false positive, caused simply by coincidence, in at least one of the 18 measurements. In this case, it turned out to have been speed of weight loss, so that was what was reported.

There are a few problems with this story that should have been spotted such as the absence of references online to 'Johannes Bohannon, PhD', the person cited as being behind the research, or to the Institute of Diet and Health that he set up for the project. Also, while there is considerable detail in the paper about the people involved in the study, it does not say how many of them there were, which is a fairly basic piece of information. On the other hand, there has been some criticism of the way John Bohannon decided to try to fool members of the public in order to show that it is easy to fool members of the public. I hope that people deliberately setting out to mislead people in this way are rare. And it is a salutary lesson in the importance of checking sample sizes and ignoring diet research that has only involved small numbers of people.

One of my favourite suggested correlations came with the news that the head of NHS England had decided to ban the sale of super-sized chocolate bars in hospitals. A spokesperson for the biggest operators of shops in hospitals was quoted in the papers saying that by introducing such schemes early, sales of sushi and salad had been boosted by 55 per cent, while fruit sales were up one quarter. The implication there is that customers looked at the range of snacks available, noticed there were no 'King Size' chocolate bars, and decided to buy sushi instead, which is a difficult scenario to imagine. Actually, it turns out that they no longer make King Size bars – they are often called 'Duo' now, so people can pretend they are going to share it with a friend – like 'Sharing Bags' of crisps. Following further enquiries it turned out that what the hospital retailers had actually said was that they had introduced a whole 'Healthier Choices' programme and a range of ways to encourage people to eat healthier snacks, so it wasn't just the banning of enormous chocolate bars that had done it.

There is a cartoon I love from the webcomic *xkcd* in which one person says: 'I used to think correlation implied causation. Then I took a statistics class. Now I don't.' His friend says: 'Sounds like the class helped.'

'Well, maybe,' the first speaker replies.

What else is going on?

It's important to point out that the problem with confusing correlation and cause is not just about missing the possibility that the two things are a coincidence. It may also be that there is something else going on. Radio 4's fabulous *More or Less* team mocked up a story about how mobile-phone masts were increasing the birth rate. They had found a correlation between the number of masts in an area and the number of babies born. It turned out that for every extra mobile-phone mast in an area, there were 17.6 more babies born per year than the national average. Is there just something romantic about masts protruding from the countryside?, the programme asked. There is no question that the two things are correlated and it's not a coincidence either. Telecoms companies tend to put more mobile-phone masts in areas where lots of people live so they can get a mobile signal. There are also more births in areas where lots of people live, for reasons that should not need explaining. So there is a link, but there is an extra step that needs to be taken before it makes any sense.

It may be that the correlation you are looking at is just a coincidence. That's a good assumption with which to start. But the next question to ask is whether, as is the case with the mobile-phone masts, there is something else going on – another step to take.

I had a letter from my son's school talking about its poor attendance record (the school as a whole, not just my son). The letter said: 'While we would never claim a direct causal link, statistics suggest that improving your attendance by 1 per cent could lead to a 5–6 per cent improvement in your attainment.'

I am certainly glad that they did not claim a direct causal link, but the wording of it and similar statements from the Department for Education is certainly meant to imply that one thing may be leading to the other. It is particularly tricky because the letter was complaining about the high levels of applications for planned absence. It does not appear to distinguish between approved absences and children just not turning up on a particular day for whatever reason. It seems likely that there is another step in this process. Having the sort of stable family life that means you are being told to get out of bed and go to school every day is likely to be causing other things that are good for your educational attainment such as being encouraged to do homework. While having a great deal of unauthorised absence would suggest you might not be getting this sort of support at home, that is not the case with authorised absence. The Department for Education's statistics show that pupils eligible for free school meals – generally taken as the indicator of whether pupils are from low-income families – are on average absent from school more. At Key Stage 2 (although not for other age groups) it turned out that pupils who had more authorised absence achieved a moderately better than average level of attainment, although again I would caution against any suggestion that there was a causal link. So the question to ask yourself is whether the reason some pupils achieve lower levels of attainment if they miss a few days of school is because there were crucial lessons being taught on those days or because there might have been some other reason why they missed school such as ill health or a chaotic home life that is also lowering their attainment. My son's school may have a poor attendance record, but it doesn't have a poor academic record.

Another aspect of the question about what else is going on is whether you're considering a causal link the wrong way round. The government is looking into whether there should be limits to the amount that teenagers use smartphones. It has cited an increase in anxiety among girls as justification for this. There have been studies suggesting that teenagers who spend excessive time on their phones are more likely to be anxious or depressed, but you could just as well argue that teenagers who are anxious or depressed are more likely to spend excessive time on their phones. The main trouble with this is that almost all teenagers use mobile phones, so while more depressed teenagers are likely to use phones, so are ones who are not depressed. You particularly need to look out for this factor before blaming something on universal activities. For example, most children are vaccinated, so most children who end up with various ailments have had those vaccines. Just demonstrating the correlation is not enough – many children who have been vaccinated do not suffer from those ailments. Without an RCT or an understanding of the mechanism by which one thing causes another, you have to assume that it's a coincidence.

Are the numbers oddly specific?

An aspect of the story about people with head injuries that should make you wonder what is going on is the fact that the period being considered was the 13 years after somebody had been in hospital with a head injury. Why would you be interested in the following 13 years? If you were choosing parameters before starting the research you would surely choose 10 or 15 years. The choice of 13 years suggests that the time period may have been chosen to give the most extreme results. That's not the only possibility, of course – it may be that data is only available for the last 13 years and the researchers were keen to use as much of it as possible.

But it is easy to look at a chart of something over time, pick the highest point and the lowest point and claim a trend, while ignoring what happened before or afterwards.

Look out for periods such as 13 years, which you could describe as 'oddly specific'; this was also the name of a now defunct website that was full of examples of figures that were surprisingly precise. There was a picture on it with an American-style road sign saying that the speed limit was 15¾. I'm sure it had been Photoshopped because there was a sign behind it that said 'Beware of signs', but it makes the point. Sometimes you expect a round number and if you don't get one you should wonder why.

While I was thinking about this subject I went for a walk round the block and it turned out that my local estate agent had a big sign up with a picture of a bottle of champagne saying 'Celebrating 28 years. Please ask us about our special celebratory offers.' I had never thought of the twenty-eighth anniversary as a particularly important one. I found a website suggesting that in parts of southern Europe it's the amber anniversary and that you could celebrate it with the gift of an orchid. But what the sign makes me think is that the estate agent is not cutting its profit margin to celebrate its significant birthday but that it's just trying to get you through the door. I know, I'm a desperately cynical man and I should take joy in helping my local estate agent celebrate, but the oddly specific number put me right off.

The sense that these things sound funny clearly kicks in early in life. My six-year-old dashed into the kitchen the other day, laughing himself silly, to inform me that he was watching 'The Simpsons' 138th Episode Spectacular'.

Here's another one: there was an advert on the London Underground for a dating website. It claimed that the site had led to 144,000 Britons being in relationships, adding 'that's 2,208 Tube carriages of people!' I wonder why 2208, given that means there are 65.2 people in each carriage. Would fewer people have signed up for the service if they had thought it had only got 2200 carriages full of people into relationships? I am a happily married man and would not have been signing up either way, but presumably there are people out there who are as pedantic about numbers as I am, but still single – I know it's hard to believe.

Oddly specific numbers are sometimes jarring because they do things with figures that are too precise for the context. This is particularly the case for forecasts – if somebody tells you that something will cost the economy a certain amount over the next decade to the nearest pound, you know they are overstretching the accuracy of their model (leaving aside the bogus nature of all such predictions, which we discussed earlier).

There was a report in 2018 that suggested pro-Leave orchestrated bots on Twitter could have created a mismatch between Leave and Remain content on Twitter that translated into 1.76 percentage points of difference in the actual voting. The same thing in the US presidential election helped Donald Trump by 3.23 percentage points. The mechanism between content being shared on Twitter and people going out and voting seems dubious at best, but to suggest that it can be cited to the nearest 0.01 of a percentage point feels as if it's pushing the point considerably further than is justified.

A wine grower came on Radio 4 during the heat-wave summer of 2018 and said that English wine producers were exporting to 'over 26' countries worldwide. If that's making you wonder what the actual number was then you are getting the hang of this. If it is 27 then why not say 27? If it is 28 then why not say it was over 27? If you're using 'over' then the number really needs to be a round one, otherwise it is oddly specific.

You can hear yourself when it sounds strange. If you were saying that something in France had cost you about 100 euros you wouldn't convert that to £88.15 because the number you were starting with wasn't that precise. You would say it had been about 100 euros, which is about £90.

The main things to remember when you're being told that something is causing something else are that your first assumption needs to be that it's a coincidence, and if there is a link, you need to ask what else is going on. Has immigration increased youth unemployment or was there a recession going on at the time that might have had something to do with it? Be particularly careful when the causal link you are examining is something you really want to believe – something that matches your existing beliefs, such as the reports about chocolate accelerating weight loss. This is also why you need to be careful with research conducted by charities. Charities do excellent work, but sometimes the statistics they release are a bit weak. Our brains are already programmed to look for patterns and assign causes, so if on top of that we want to believe what is being said because we like the organisation, then we need to be on our guard. After reading this chapter, I hope you are ready to be wary of correlation being dressed as causation. That may be a result of the advice the chapter contains or it may just be a coincidence.

CHAPTER 8

Alarm-bell Phrases

What to look out for

There are various words and phrases that should set off alarm bells in your head every time you see or hear them. They don't necessarily mean that the figures you are about to hear are wrong or misleading, but they make it more likely. You will see them in adverts and the news, you will hear them from politicians and you should take them as a hint that you may be being misled. Understanding the numbers properly is all about seeing the warning signs at the right time, because you can then choose to ignore a story completely or seek more information. Some of these phrases come up regularly, such as 'sickie' statistics every time there is a major sporting event taking place. Others may be hidden in important speeches, where you wouldn't notice them if you were not on your guard. Once you start listening out for certain phrases, you'll find them all over the place.

Up to

'Up to' is a widely used and generally misleading weasel phrase, which means that the figure with which you are being presented is the maximum possible. Those signs on the high street saying 'Always up to 60 per cent less' seem to me a copper-bottomed guarantee that the shop will never discount anything by more than 60 per cent. It does not mean that anything in the shop is actually reduced by 60 per cent. In fact, it doesn't necessarily mean that anything in the shop has been reduced at all, just that nothing has been cut by more than 60 per cent.

Similarly, I saw a sign in a department store saying 'Our gift to you. Up to 30 per cent off selected lines'. You won't be surprised to hear that '30 per cent off' was in about 500 point, bold lettering, while 'up to' and 'selected lines' were in about 10 point. But the 'selected lines' disclaimer is interesting, because presumably it could mean that non-selected lines will be more than 30 per cent off.

We know that this is the sort of thing that retailers do and we have become used to it, but when it gets into the news it's a problem, especially when it spoils one of my favourite stories. *Metro* reported in December 2012 that South Yorkshire Police had spent £7000 on 280 cardboard cutouts of officers in an attempt to deter thieves. 'The cardboard officers have reduced crime by up to 50 per cent in some areas,' the paper said. First of all, I'm dying to know how South Yorkshire Police demonstrated that any fall in crime was due to the presence of cardboard officers and not other factors. But secondly, we don't know from that report that crime has been reduced at all, only that crime has not been reduced by more than 50 per cent in some areas. And it follows that it has been reduced by more than 50 per cent in other areas.

More seriously, the Conservative Party manifesto in 2017 promised to recruit 'up to 10,000 more mental health professionals', a promise that the government can keep as long as it does not recruit more than 10,000. At the same election, the Liberal Democrats pledged to: 'create a new designation of national nature parks to protect up to one million acres of accessible green space'. When making election promises it seems to me that a minimum number would be more appropriate than a maximum.

There are many other similarly unhelpful expressions, including 'as much as', which means the same thing as 'up to', and 'at least', which is the opposite. If you are not interested in the maximum or minimum levels for a particular figure, then don't use them.

As if the regular use of 'up to' wasn't bad enough, it's often used in ways that make it even worse. Buzzfeed ran a headline saying: 'As many as 300 managers at BBC News earn up to £77,000 or more, according to a leaked document.' To break down what that means, there are no more than 300 managers who are earning either more than £77,000 or less than £77,000. That's not a newsworthy revelation.

'Sickie' statistics

You would not believe the number of times you see statistics used with great confidence to trumpet the number of people doing something they shouldn't. It is remarkably difficult to collect such figures because people tend to go out of their way to prevent anyone finding out.

I often receive emails from PR firms claiming to have discovered how many people are planning to 'take a sickie' on a particular day, usually when there is an event such as an important football game happening in the middle of a weekday. These figures are based on surveys. I look forward to the day that someone phones me to ask whether I'm planning to call in sick so I can watch England playing on the television. Are there really people who say yes? The survey results I'm sent suggest there must be. The follow-up to the number of people planning to take an unjustified sick-day is always how much that will be costing the economy, but you already know from Chapter 3 that such claims are dubious.

The sick-day story is frivolous and (I hope) mainly harmless, but the same principle goes for figures about illegal activities. Some statistics on law-breaking come from reports or surveys of the victims, which is fair enough although still not an exact science. But take a hefty pinch of salt with figures such as illegal migration, illegal downloads or using mobile phones while driving.

Record numbers

We all love a record. When someone wins Olympic gold, breaking the record is a cherry on the top of their achievement and you will find me cheering as much as anyone. But most aspects of life are not like the Olympics. You achieve your record age every second. Populations tend to grow and prices tend to rise, which means that you would regularly expect there to be record numbers of people doing things and that record amounts will be spent on things, both by governments and individuals. Prime Minister Theresa May regularly talks about how record amounts of money are going into education, which may be a surprise for people with school-age children who keep hearing how short of cash their local schools are. While the amount of money in the pot for schools in England is indeed at a record high, rising pupil numbers and prices mean that schools are going to have to make savings of approximately 8 per cent of their budgets by 2020. Record spending is not necessarily good enough because the things that schools spend money on would be expected to get more expensive every year: teachers, buildings, heating, lighting, books and stationery are all likely to cost more. And there was a baby boom in the early 2000s, which is working its way through the school system. What you need to know is what has happened to spending per pupil after you have adjusted for rising prices (inflation).

Death tolls

When you hear figures for the number of people killed by a disaster, think about how those statistics have been collected. I remember seeing pictures in the days after the Boxing Day tsunami in 2004, in which whole towns had been washed away, and yet the official death tolls were still only about 10,000 – the eventual figure was more than 200,000. Anybody in the area trying to help has better things to do than try to come up with an accurate figure for the numbers of people who have died.

Remember the controversy about the number of people who died in the appalling Grenfell Tower fire of 14 June 2017 in London? These were official police death-toll figures, which were announced as 12 people, then later 30 people, gradually rising to the final figure of 71. The police went to extraordinary lengths to make sure they were certain before announcing somebody had died, searching every flat in the building for human remains, which was made very difficult by the damage caused by the ferocity of the fire. When you hear official police figures early on, they are likely to be conservative, for perfectly good reasons.

There is considerable uncertainty about death tolls in war zones. The figures for the numbers of people killed in Syria vary wildly, while the best estimates for the numbers killed in Yemen are based on figures from hospitals, even though many of the hospitals have closed as a result of the conflict and much of the fighting happened in rural areas that never had hospitals.

This isn't just a problem for death-toll figures – any statistics are hard to collect in conflict zones. It is difficult to find a representative sample for a survey in a developed country that is at peace. Imagine how much more difficult it would be to do so in a war zone.

International comparisons

Headline writers love being able to compare statistics between countries, but it's a dangerous thing to do. Take the headlines in March 2015 claiming that people in Rwanda can expect to live more years in good health than the most deprived 10 per cent of people in England. The figures for Rwanda came from the World Health Organization (WHO), which found that people born in the country in 2012 had a healthy life expectancy of 55 years, which was a remarkable improvement, given that in 2000 the figure was 40.

Journalists then compared that with figures from the Office for National Statistics (ONS), which looked at the inequality in healthy life expectancies between rich and poor people in England. It found that the most deprived 10 per cent of the population had a healthy life expectancy of 52 years, while the least deprived 10 per cent could expect 71 healthy years. That's a shocking range, but does the comparison with Rwanda work?

To check, you can look at the WHO research. It also gave a figure for the UK, which it said had a healthy life expectancy of 71, the same figure that the ONS was giving for the best-off 10 per cent in England.

This should make you wonder if the two studies, while using the same terminology, used different methods. And that was indeed the case. The WHO figures were based on a detailed survey about people's health and used the answers to subtract years of ill-health from existing life-expectancy figures. The ONS used the results from its Annual Population Survey, which asked respondents if their health was very good, good, fair, bad or very bad. It turned out that people were more likely to classify themselves as being in ill-health under the ONS system than they were to be classified as being in ill-health based on the answers they gave to the WHO. That means that the comparison between deprived people in England and everyone in Rwanda does not stand up. The WHO also warned about the difficulties of conducting such research in low-income countries, which also makes such international comparisons difficult.

If you really need to make international comparisons, see if you can get a big, global organisation to do it for you: the World Bank, the United Nations and suchlike are good at this sort of thing. Their websites are less user-hostile than they used to be and their statistics divisions are very helpful.

Straw poll

When a poll or survey is dubious or inaccurate people try to justify this by saying it's just a straw poll or a snapshot. What that means is that the methodology is not good enough but they are going to try to get away with it anyway. It's 'just a bit of fun' in Peter Snow's words. But if the results are being used to try to convince the public that opinion is in one direction or another then it's serious. I am told the term 'straw poll' comes from the idea of holding up a piece of straw to establish which way the wind is blowing, which seems like a more robust methodology than you see from straw polls.

Remember the morning after the general election in 2017, many outlets reported that there had been 72 per cent turnout among 18-to-24-year-olds? This was the start of the 'youthquake', which ended up being the *Oxford Dictionary* word of the year. The figure was tweeted by Labour MP David Lammy and also by National Union of Students president Malia Bouattia, who said she was not surprised. I was certainly surprised given that the pollsters at Ipsos Mori estimated that only 43 per cent of that age group had voted in 2010 and 44 per cent in 2015. The figure was eventually tracked down to Alex Cairns, who ran an organisation trying to encourage young people to vote – he stressed that the figure was 'an indication' based on conversations he had conducted with student union presidents and other research that he had done. So we can add 'an indication' to the list of alarm-bell phrases.

We never find out exactly how many people from any particular age group vote in a general election because it's a secret ballot, but the best indication we get is from the British Election Study, which concluded in January 2018 that there had been little change in youth turnout between 2015 and 2017, with the margin of error meaning that it could have risen a bit or fallen a bit.

These words and phrases should put you on your guard, but they do not mean that what you are reading is definitely nonsense. One straw poll that was entirely robust came from Pig World, the voice of the British pig industry. It was wondering how much rising straw prices were hitting the margins of pig farmers, so it told its reporter at the British Pig and Poultry Fair to go and ask some of them what they thought. The reporter said she had spoken to farmers who were being squeezed by the price rise. There was no attempt to use these conversations to come up with any questionable stats and the publication ran with the headline: 'Straw poll highlights concerns over a straw-based future'. Excellent work.

Statistically significant

Statistically significant is a technical term, which means that the findings are outside the margin of error. You need to be careful not to confuse that with something being significant, meaning important. By convention, if a finding in a piece of research is statistically significant it means that if that same research were to be conducted 20 times, that finding would turn up at least 19 times. Remember that the more people you ask in your survey or the more patients you have in your study, the more likely your findings are to be statistically significant because the margin of error gets smaller. A really huge study will probably find lots of things that are statistically significant, but that doesn't mean they matter.

In a speech in 2017, Royal Statistical Society president Sir David Spiegelhalter gave the example of research suggesting that watching television for more than five hours a night increased your chances of having a fatal pulmonary embolism, compared with watching less than two and a half hours. But he added that when you looked at the absolute level of risk, it 'could be translated as meaning that you can expect to watch more than five hours of television a night for 12,000 years before experiencing the event, which somewhat lessens the impact'. So the effect may have been statistically significant, but it may not have been very relevant to people's lives. This is not to say that watching five hours of television a night is not bad for you in other ways – just that you can expect other problems to manifest themselves considerably earlier than the blocked arteries in the lungs.

Prof. Spiegelhalter also warns against assuming that if doing an enormous amount of something is bad for you, doing a little bit of it will also be. Look out for that logic in health-related articles.

Beware of the word 'significant' with any qualifier attached such as 'borderline significant', 'potentially significant' or even 'practically significant'. A one-in-

20 chance of your findings being a coincidence is not setting the bar particularly high. If the research can't even get over that bar then it's almost certainly not good enough. Also, 19 out of 20, or 95 per cent confidence, is a pretty standard place to set the bar. If you read something that is trying to set it at 90 per cent or lower you should be wondering why.

People asking not to be named

Anonymous sources have their place. If a journalist is interviewing victims of crime or even perpetrators of crime it's generally pretty obvious why people would want to remain anonymous. But if it's a story littered with anonymous sources and it's harder to work out why they would want their names withheld, you should be on your guard. One of the wire services used to have a reporter covering energy prices who came up with colourful quotes from unnamed oil traders such as: 'the blood is in the water and the sharks are getting frenzied'. They used to brighten my days, but I did wonder why he was having to quote unnamed traders. Did he have a friend who was coming up with these lines but wasn't really allowed to talk to the press or was he just making them up himself?

Exclusive statistics

'Exclusive' is an overused word in news that makes me wonder who is being excluded and why. Sometimes it's obvious why an article is called an exclusive – some hard-working journalist has managed to find something out or get access to something or someone, and has used this to come up with a story that nobody else has. But when you hear that a news organisation has been given exclusive access to a particular data set, you should probably wonder why. Working in a busy newsroom, you become attuned to the signs that a press release is going to contain unreliable figures, and one of the key indicators is that the organisation sending it to you is prepared to offer you exclusive access to it. Sometimes the lure of an exclusive story is enough to make journalists let down their guard and run some questionable figures of which they would otherwise have disposed. Again, this does not necessarily mean that a statistic is nonsense, but it should put you on your guard.

I don't have to look far back in my inbox to find 'new research' (I hardly ever get sent old research) being offered to me as an exclusive. Top of the list is the revelation that 'over two-thirds (64 per cent) of Generation Z say salary is their top motivator in the workplace'. What a great story, even once you get past the belief that 64 per cent is more than two-thirds. I decided against publishing a BBC exclusive revealing that members of Generation Z like being paid to work.

Television viewing figures

TV viewing figures are another one of those statistics that sound like they are a precise count of a total number of people, but are in fact based on a survey. Five thousand households with 12,000 individuals log their viewing habits and the figures are then extrapolated to cover the whole of the population. Especially with so many channels available, it means that one or two people changing their viewing habits may have an enormous impact on the ratings for a particular programme. This is not the case for online traffic though. On my second day working for the BBC News website, I received an email telling me precisely how many times the article I had written the day before had been clicked on. It was terribly exciting, especially having come from television where no such precision exists.

Even though the Barb television rating system used in the UK is based on a survey, it's a pretty big survey. The figures from it are certainly more robust than the figures you see now and then for the number of people watching particular sporting events around the world. I have seen claims that the Tour de France is watched by 4 billion, 3.5 billion and 1.6 billion people.

Another figure to be deeply suspicious of is how many records a particular artist has sold around the world, which are widely reported, usually when they die. These global figures simply weren't collected, especially in the early careers of some of the ageing rockers we find ourselves mourning. The figures are desperately unreliable and may be considered estimates at best.

Comparisons over a long time

Early in the 2016 EU referendum campaign, Michael Gove claimed that the proportion of UK trade done with the EU was lower than it had been before the UK joined the EU. I ended up in London's Guildhall Library, working my way through the five volumes of the 1972 edition of the *Annual Statement of the Overseas Trade of the United Kingdom*. Then over the weekend I realised I had ignored trade in services and would have to dig up a separate publication called *Britain's Invisible Exports*. At that point a friendly economic historian took pity on me and helped me find the right figures on a United Nations database, and I could establish that the proportion of trade with the EU had not fallen as claimed.

This brought home to me how spoiled I am when I try to find out how much a statistic has changed since last year, or over five years, when I can just look online. Some departments at the ONS in Newport still proudly display their huge, leather-bound volumes of historic statistics, but I don't generally have to use hard copies.

There are problems with making comparisons over long periods of time. In the same way as indicators with the same name differ from country to country, so the methodology for indicators in one country may change over time. There may be warnings that series are not continuous when there have been big changes, but it is still easy to be caught out. For example, the Census for England and Wales, which is conducted every ten years, asks how many rooms a household has. In 1971, respondents were told not to include kitchens that were less than six feet wide. In 1981 and 1991, kitchens less than six feet six inches were ignored. In 2001 and 2011, all kitchens counted as rooms, so if you look at the whole series, it will look as if rooms per household increased more than they actually did, because more small kitchens were being included.

Two of my favourite recent claims including very long time series are that pay growth was at its slowest since the Napoleonic wars and that governments since 2010 had borrowed more money than all Labour governments put together. Both of them were fun to check because I got to talk to economic historians and use the Bank of England's excellent 'Millennium of Macroeconomic Data' research data set. Nonetheless, earnings figures from the 1800s are sketchy at best and trying to compare borrowing by the Ramsay

MacDonald government in 1924 with borrowing by the coalition government in 2010 ignores all sorts of changes to the country and its economy.

When you see claims that something is the worst it has been for hundreds of years, take them with a suitably large pinch of salt.

Official statistics

We hear many references to official statistics, but what does that mean? The gold standard of statistics in the UK are national statistics – they are easy to spot because they have a kitemark with a tick, saying 'national statistics' on it. The rules governing how they are produced and presented are strict. Every now and then a national statistic loses its kitemark because of concerns about its methodology. The point is, national statistics are tightly policed – while they are not perfect they are probably the best-available figures. Government departments also produce what are called 'official statistics', which are still governed by the Code of Practice for statistics but might not be quite as robust or as important. Other figures released by government departments are not necessarily as reliable, and journalists who are short of time may accidentally describe them as official just because they have come from the government. The trouble with these other releases is that ministers may get involved in which figures are placed most prominently and there may not be consistency across publications. You should be as suspicious of a set of figures from a government department that does not classify as an official statistic as you would be about numbers from any other organisation.

Poverty statistics

When you see figures for poverty they will either be measuring absolute poverty or relative poverty. Relative poverty tends to mean that a household has an income after taxes and benefits that is less than 60 per cent of the median income. Remember, the median income is the one that half of households are above and half of households are below. These figures are generally also adjusted for the size of the household because a bigger household needs more to live on. There are advantages to this measure – it tells you whether a household is able to afford things that other households can. But it throws up odd situations, such as if the economy is doing really badly then the median income is likely to fall, which means that a household may suddenly be lifted out of relative poverty, not because it's better off but because lots of other households are worse off.

Absolute poverty is generally considered to be a situation in which someone cannot afford basic necessities such as food, clothing and shelter, but that's not how the UK government sees it. Its measure of absolute poverty is the same as the measure of relative poverty except that instead of using the median income at the time, it uses the median income from 2010–11. This makes things a bit confusing. All I can suggest is that when you hear about changes in the number of people living in poverty, make sure you know what measure people are talking about.

You should be wary of figures for global inequality. In particular, some of the highest-profile measures of wealth inequality allow for negative wealth, which means that the poorest people are not those living with almost nothing in slums, they are people with enormous mortgages living in huge houses, or those with considerable student debt who might nonetheless have high-paying jobs. These are not generally the people you think of as being at the bottom of the global wealth pile.

Underlying

I don't want to talk too much here about company results, but there are a few key alarm-bell words to listen out for when chief executives tell you how their companies have been doing, and they are 'adjusted' and 'underlying'. The rules for preparing financial results are designed to use a number of fairly arbitrary assumptions to make one company's results broadly comparable with another's. But company bosses like to claim that the message you are getting from the usual headline figures such as pre-tax profits or net earnings is not really telling you what's going on in the company, so they produce 'adjusted' figures, which are supposed to tell you about the 'underlying' performance of the business.

Sometimes this is fair enough. If a company has finally decided to write off all the money it spent on a misguided takeover five years ago, which means that it has to report an overall loss of many billions of pounds, it may also be useful to have a figure excluding that write-off so that you can see how the rest of the business has been doing.

On the other hand, sometimes you get the feeling that the adjustments are not being made to help you understand the business, and the more things that are excluded or adjusted for, the more likely it is that you are not seeing the full picture.

There was an American company providing serviced office space, which tried to focus on a figure it called community-adjusted EBITDA. EBITDA is a fairly standard earnings figure, excluding factors such as interest payments, tax and the falling value of things such as buildings and equipment (it stands for 'earnings before interest, taxes, depreciation and amortisation'). But the community-adjusted bit meant that they were also excluding the amount they were paying their employees, advertising expenses and the costs of opening up in new locations. The community-adjusted EBITDA figure was positive, suggesting the business was profitable, unlike the overall earnings figure, which showed a net loss of almost $900 million.

Maybe the company is right, and its huge profitability is being masked by various items that do not really affect the strength of the business. But it certainly suggested to me that further investigation was needed.

Once you start listening out for certain words and phrases you will hear them all the time. They are an excellent way of reminding you that you might be being misled and should either look a bit further into the claim being made, or ignore it and get on with your day. In particular, now you know to be wary of phrases such as 'up to', 'straw poll' and 'adjusted', you can start thinking about how some statistics try to quantify things that are difficult to ascertain. It can mean that both the statistics you are presented with and any others with which they are being compared may be skewed.

CHAPTER 9

Risk and Uncertainty

How likely is that not to be true?

In February 2014 there was confusion about the UK unemployment figures, which meant that some news organisations were reporting that the unemployment rate had fallen to 7.2 per cent and some were reporting that it had risen to 7.2 per cent. It had actually fallen, despite the previous month's figure having been lower. You may think this is unreasonably confusing and you would be right.

This chapter is about uncertainty, risk and chance, which are hugely important parts of statistics but get less attention than they deserve. When you see big statistical claims being made strongly in the headlines, you should consider carefully whether they are justified. Many of the statistical methods behind those claims will not be good enough to provide anything more than an estimate, but the words used will suggest unjustified precision. The flip side of asking how likely something is to be true is asking how likely it is not to be true, which is all about getting across the uncertainty involved. When we talk about how likely things are to happen, we are talking about risk; understanding and communicating levels of risk is one of the great challenges facing statisticians, journalists and politicians. Nobody has really cracked it yet, but if you understand where some people are getting it wrong and how others are trying to get it right, you will be in a much better position to know what is going on.

The three tools you need in this area are:

- Using measures of uncertainty to find out if a story is really a story

- Making sure you see both absolute risk and percentage changes

- Deciding whether the odds of more than one thing happening are being considered correctly

Using measures of uncertainty to find out if a story is really a story

When you see the unemployment figures published each month, you may think it's a precise count of the number of people who would like to have a job and do not have one, but it's not – it's based on a survey. That's a perfectly normal way of measuring unemployment, and the current UK unemployment statistics are the best-available figures. But it's important to understand what the methodology does to how precise the figures are.

Almost all of the UK's official statistics are based on taking a sample and assuming the rest of the country has broadly the same features as the chosen few. In fact, the ONS baby-names statistics are among the small number of figures that are based on counting everyone involved with no extrapolation. That means you can tell exactly how many babies were called a particular name in each year, as long as there were three or more of them. I can tell you that there were precisely 6259 baby boys named Oliver in England and Wales in 2017, and 3 named Oliver-John.

Most of the more important UK statistics, though, are an estimate and it is important to use the correct language about them so as not to sound too precise. Let's start thinking about the uncertainty involved by going back and looking at why unemployment figures have been unreasonably confusing. To do that, we need to look at how the figures are collected.

Unemployment statistics

The headline figure for unemployment used to be the number of people claiming unemployment benefits, which is called the claimant count, but then it was realised that the government could fiddle the numbers by moving people onto different benefits such as disability benefits. The new Universal Credit system makes the claimant count even harder to assess in terms of unemployment, because some Universal Credit claimants are employed and some are unemployed. As a result, the claimant count has lost its status as a national statistic. To get away from just counting the number of claimants, for many years the ONS has used an internationally agreed definition of unemployment as its headline figure: somebody is unemployed if they do not have a job, have tried to find a job in the last four weeks and is available to start work in the next two weeks.

To work out that figure, the ONS conducts a Labour Force Survey (LFS), a huge survey in which it talks to about 40,000 households containing 100,000 individuals every three months. It starts with staff going and knocking on people's doors all over the country, with follow-up calls coming from a call centre at the ONS offices in Titchfield, on the south coast of England. You may have seen a documentary series on BBC Three called *The Call Centre*, which followed the activities of Nev Wilshire, the boss of a Swansea call centre, and his staff of mainly 20-somethings as they battle to get out of bed and get anybody on the phone to talk to them. Well, the

ONS call centre in Titchfield is nothing at all like that. For a start, it's mainly staffed by older women who have been working there for years. I visited a few years ago and listened into some calls. It's completely unlike the sort of cold-calling you usually hear from people conducting surveys. The people they call are expecting to be rung and seem to have a relationship with the system.

The point is, this is a seriously high-quality survey, but it's still a survey, which means that there is a margin of error. The ONS is very good at telling us what the margin of error is for all of the measures in the labour market report. It does that with the use of confidence intervals, which show the range of values within which it thinks the actual figure is likely to be. So, for example, the figure for the change in unemployment generally has a 95 per cent confidence interval of about 75,000, which means the ONS is 95 per cent confident that the actual change in the number of people unemployed is within plus or minus 75,000 of the figure they have given. If the change in unemployment is smaller than that confidence interval, the figure is described as not being statistically significant, which means we can't say that unemployment has either risen or fallen. If you look at all the figures for 2017, there is not a single month when the change in unemployment is significant. Any headline you saw that year based on quarterly figures that said UK unemployment had risen or fallen was misusing the statistics.

Another thing that makes these figures tricky is that they are quarterly statistics – they cover a three-month period – but they are released every month. So the January to March figures will be published in May and then the February to April figures will be published in June, and so on. That's because the people who ask the questions from the Titchfield call centre have the households they are surveying divided equally over the 13 weeks of the quarter. It means that two-thirds of the data used each month was also used the previous month. Each month's figures will be based on one-third of the respondents having been asked since the last figures were released and two-thirds of respondents for whom they are still using the answers they gave in the previous two months. As a result, you shouldn't be comparing this month's figures with last month's figures – you should be comparing them with the ones that were released three months ago.

This brings us back to the situation described at the beginning of the chapter. The ONS reported that the unemployment rate for October to December 2013 was 7.2 per cent. Some news outlets reported that as an unexpected rise, because they were comparing it with the previous month's figure (covering September to November) of 7.1 per cent. But the figure was comparable not with the previous month's figure but the one for the previous quarter, July to September, which was 7.6 per cent.

The system of reporting rolling quarters every month does make life difficult for journalists trying to report the figures. Up until the late 1990s, unemployment was reported once a quarter, but then it was realised that the figures could be released monthly without having to collect any extra data. There are ways round the problem. One of them would be to triple the number of people interviewed in the Labour Force Survey, but that would be eye-wateringly expensive. If the government was thinking of injecting a bit of extra cash into the collection of employment statistics, it's also worth bearing in mind that even doubling the number of households surveyed would only make the change in unemployment correct to plus or minus about 55,000 instead of about 75,000. Another option would be to headline the change in unemployment compared with a year earlier instead of the previous quarter, which does give you lots more significant changes but also makes the statistics feel less current. Or, as a drastic measure, news organisations could consider only reporting the unemployment figures when there has been a statistically significant change, but I can't see that happening.

High-profile statistics

Unemployment is one of the most closely watched statistics published each month. Other figures that always get lots of attention are inflation, migration and GDP, all of which involve some sampling.

The inflation figure tells us how much prices are rising. It is based on a notional basket of goods and is the figure targeted by the Bank of England's interest rate-setting Monetary Policy Committee. The statistical authorities decide what is a normal range of items to buy in a month and then look at how the prices of those things have changed in a range of outlets. It's a sample of the changes in prices across the economy. If you buy a drastically different range of products to the ones the statisticians have chosen, or indeed use different suppliers, then you will experience a different rate of inflation.

The migration figures are based on asking a selection of travellers at ports whether they are planning to come to the country or leave the country for at least a year. If you think that's an inaccurate way of working out migration, and indeed the population, then you're not alone. Its accuracy is sensitive to factors such as people changing their plans, refusing to be interviewed, lying or arriving at ports where there are not ONS staff asking questions. For example, many of the passengers arriving from eastern Europe in the mid-2000s were coming to smaller, regional airports, where the International Passenger Survey had no representatives. Just as with unemployment, the sampling method means that the rise or fall in immigration has to be pretty large to be statistically significant, so we can't always say with confidence whether migration has risen or fallen.

The early estimates of GDP, perhaps the most influential economic statistic, rely heavily on extrapolating what's happened to the economy based on actual results from a relatively small proportion of companies. By the time the figures have had their fourth or fifth estimate and are based on more actual returns from businesses and fewer estimates, it's probably too late to change everyone's perception of what is going on in the economy, and may be too late to change any measures taken by governments or central banks based on what they had been told was going on.

To be fair, the ONS is in the process of carrying out all sorts of interesting research into how it can use other sources of data to improve the accuracy and speed of its statistics. You could use records from GP surgeries to improve population data or scrape prices from supermarket websites to help with the inflation data. They probably will eventually find a way to get a reliable claimant-count figure from Universal Credit and maybe there is some hi-tech system we haven't yet thought of that will give more accurate, monthly figures for unemployment without having to spend millions of pounds extra on collecting them. As I mentioned when talking about surveys, the most accurate data would come from asking everybody in the country, but that takes ages and costs a fortune, so we need to accept that getting affordable figures reasonably quickly means they will not be absolutely precise.

Less helpful measures

Although the confidence intervals make the UK unemployment figures more difficult to report, they are at least clear and reasonably easy to understand, unlike an alternative measure: coefficients of variation or CVs for short. I hope you never have to deal with one of these, but just in case you do, a CV is an indicator of the quality of a figure – the smaller the CV the higher the quality. They are presented as percentages, and the true value is likely to lie within plus or minus twice the CV. Why would anyone create a measure like this? As an example, if you had a figure of 200 with a CV of 5 per cent, it would mean the actual figure is likely to be between 180 and 220.

I first came across these when I was head of statistics at BBC News and was asked to look at some figures that were the basis of a report due to go out on the *Six O'clock News* that evening. We had been sent figures by Labour suggesting that there had been big falls in average weekly earnings for women and the figures were broken down by constituency. They were based on a very big survey – the ONS's Annual Survey of Hours and Earnings (Ashe), which takes records on 1 per cent of employee jobs from PAYE records. But even the biggest surveys struggle when they are broken down into the 650 constituencies across the UK. Looking at an extreme case, the figures we were sent suggested that, in Putney, average weekly earnings for women had fallen from £460.60 a week in 2010 to £366.10 a week in 2013. That would be a staggering fall – about 20 per cent, which would be very unusual. It failed the reasonably likely to be true test, so I dug a bit further. Once you applied the CV to it, it turned out that we could actually say with 95 per cent confidence that the figure had fallen from between £343.20 and £578.00 in 2010 to between £222.60 and £509.60 in 2013. There is considerable overlap in those figures, so you can't say with confidence that wages had fallen at all. And as big as the suggested fall was, it was dwarfed by the range of the figures. That was the case for many of the numbers, especially the ones with the biggest falls that were being used as examples. We had to drop the story, which was a great shame because a lot of work had already gone into preparing it for the programme.

This story highlights another problem with wages figures, which is that they often don't tell you what you think they are telling you. In this case, we were being asked to use average weekly earnings to assess what happened to pay for women. It is a particularly unhelpful figure because women are considerably more likely to work part-time than men. If a new business had set up in the area and employed lots of women part-time but on generous hourly wages, the average weekly earnings figure would fall because the average number of hours people were working would probably fall. But that would not suggest women were being paid less. Average hourly earnings would have been more helpful or indeed a breakdown into full-time and part-time workers.

It's worth bearing in mind that we're only talking about the confidence intervals here because we're looking at some of the world's biggest and most robust surveys. Most surveys that you see, especially some of those we looked at in Chapter 1, would have margins of error off the scale.

But even when you're looking at the highest-profile statistics, it's worth considering whether the methodology is robust enough to say that something has risen or fallen in a particular month.

Making sure you see both absolute risk and percentage changes

I talked in Chapter 4 about the dangers of lonely percentages, which is the problem of being given a percentage change without the absolute figures. This is particularly a problem when you're talking about percentage risk of getting a particular disease, when there are real dangers of scaring people unnecessarily. Newspapers seem to have daily updates of what causes or prevents cancer, and it is very hard to decide whether you should be changing your behaviour without the full context.

It may feel like a bit of a handbrake turn to go from uncertainty in surveys to risk in health stories, but they are very much part of the same area of statistics – how likely something is to be accurate and how likely something is to happen.

In March 2008 there was a headline in the *Daily Mail*: 'Why eating just one sausage a day raises your cancer risk by 20 per cent'. If you read on further it turns out that the finding is that eating 50g of processed meat a day, which is one sausage or three rashers of bacon, increases your risk of getting bowel cancer by one-fifth. And then there's a photo of a schoolboy eating a sausage, although the caption points out that the picture was posed by a model, presumably because it would just be too damn dangerous to let a real schoolboy eat a sausage.

Four years later in the *Daily Express* there was a spookily similar headline: 'Daily fry-up boosts cancer risk by 20 per cent'. It's much the same story except that this time it's talking about pancreatic cancer instead of bowel cancer and they have used a close-up photo of some bacon to illustrate the story without exposing any models to processed meat danger. These headlines are scary – cancer is clearly a bad thing and 20 per cent is a big increase in the risk.

Communicating risk is not something that is done very well on the whole and the man trying to help us all to do it better is the aforementioned Professor Sir David Spiegelhalter, who runs a statistics lab in Cambridge that investigates better ways to help people understand about risk. He recommends looking at how much the level of risk has changed (the relative risk) in the context of the absolute risk. So we know that the change in the relative risk is 20 per cent, which is the difference in risk between people who don't have the extra sausage a day and those who do. But we also need to know the absolute risk: the actual numbers of people who could be affected by eating the sausage. With pancreatic cancer, 5 people out of every 400 will develop the disease in their lifetimes if they do not have that sausage a day. If they do eat a sausage or three rashers of bacon every day of their lives then that increases to 6 people. An increase from 5 people to 6 people is indeed a rise of 20 per cent, but the actual number of people sounds less alarming than the original headline. It may well be that when you understand the absolute risk you feel it is time to abandon daily bacon sandwiches, or you may feel the extra risk is worth it – we're somewhat outside my area of expertise here (I'm Jewish). The point is that you need both figures to be able to take that decision. If almost nobody is affected by a particular condition and that increases by 50 per cent then you are still left with almost nobody being affected.

Many of the other factors to look out for if you are scared by a health story in the news have been discussed in other chapters, but here are a few of the most relevant ones. I talked in Chapter 7 about questioning whether one thing is really causing another. You should also beware of reading too much into what a single study says. If it's an important piece of work then other researchers will try to investigate similar things and you will get a better idea of the quality of the work. Later, you will see research that pull together the results of many studies into similar areas, which will give a much more reliable picture.

I also talked in that chapter about randomised controlled trials, which require there to have been some sort of control over the experiment, generally allocating people to particular treatments at random. If the researchers have just observed what has happened or indeed looked back at what has happened without being involved, it is very difficult to demonstrate that one thing has caused another. You should be suspicious if researchers have not clearly decided in advance what they are looking for

and may just be fishing in the statistics for something to investigate. And remember when you're
talking about correlation to ask what else might be
going on.

When you're looking at clinical trials in health
stories, the number of people who should be
involved is not necessarily the same as it would be
in a survey. Clearly, having more people involved is
better, because it makes coincidental outcomes less
likely. But if you're studying a rare disease and there
is a huge and obvious effect from treatment then it
may be that just a handful of subjects will provide
enough information from which to draw conclusions (although many more may be needed to get
regulatory clearance). And it is important to check
whether the headline is actually justified by the
conclusions in the research, which I will discuss in
more detail in the next chapter.

Another phenomenon that is important in this
area is regression to the mean, which sounds complicated but is relatively straightforward. It's the idea
that in situations in which there are many factors
involved, an extreme result is likely to be followed
by a more normal one. If your football team wins
9–0 this Saturday in the Premier League, you would
expect a more normal one- or two-goal margin the
following week.

The phenomenon is easily explained by a game
for which I am indebted to former chair of the UK

Statistics Authority and *More or Less* presenter Sir Andrew Dilnot. He explained it in the context of a decision about whether to put speed cameras on a particular road. Everyone in the room is given two dice to roll, which represents the number of accidents on a particular road in year one. The people with the highest scores, generally 11 or 12, are declared to be accident blackspots. As a result, it is decided that speed cameras must be pointed towards them as they roll the dice a second time to find out how many accidents happen on their roads in year two. Of course, the number of accidents almost always falls, which vindicates the decision to use speed cameras. The point about regression to the mean is that in situations that may be affected by chance, such as the number of accidents there are on a road, an extreme year is likely to be followed by a less extreme one. In other words, unusually high or low numbers may return to normal just by chance.

The game may seem frivolous, but it is relevant to many decisions taken by governments. When they consider whether to take action to deal with a problem, it is likely that they will try to deal with the extreme cases. But it's possible that it's only a coincidence that these were the extreme cases, in which case you would expect a more normal outcome the following year.

This also works in health cases in which you are likely to treat the most seriously ill sufferers from a particular disease, some of whom may become closer to the average level of illness by chance even if the treatment you are trialling does not really work.

Regression to the mean was first discussed by Sir Francis Galton in 1877. One of the examples he used was the height of parents compared with their children. Tall parents tended to have children who grew up to be shorter than them, while short parents, on average, had children who grew up to be taller than them. This is because children will, on average, be average height, so you should not be surprised by the result of comparing their height with the height of very tall or very short parents.

Beware of extremes when judging measures taken by authorities. It is statistically difficult to exclude regression to the mean from a study, but if the researchers make it clear they are aware of the problem it is a good sign.

Deciding whether the odds of more than one thing happening are being considered correctly

An important question to ask when looking at the chances of more than one thing happening is whether the odds are linked or independent. If you flip a coin, the chances of getting a head are one in two. The chances of getting two heads in a row are one in four, three heads is one in eight, and so on. That is because the odds are independent so you just multiply them each time. The chances of getting tails are not related to whether you threw heads last time. But odds are not always independent – sometimes they are linked.

I was in the *More or Less* studio on the day of an item about double-yolked eggs. The British Egg Information Service tells us that the odds of finding an egg with two yolks is one in 1000. A BBC colleague had cracked four eggs in a row and found them all to have double yolks. If finding double-yolked eggs were like flipping a coin, then the odds of getting two double-yolked eggs in a row would be one in a million (a thousand times a thousand), three would be one in a billion and four would be one in a trillion, which is pretty unlikely. But that ignores the possibility that double-yolked eggs come in clusters, so that finding one in a box would make it more likely to find another. And that is indeed the case, because double-yolked eggs are more likely to come from hens of a particular age (20 to 28 weeks old), flocks of birds tend to all be of about the same age and the eggs in a box are all likely to come from the same flock. Also, double-yolked eggs will be unusually big for hens of that age, which means if you have bought a box of large eggs from a young flock, they are even more likely to have double yolks. The excitement in the studio was overwhelming as my colleague cracked the last two eggs from her carton and they both turned out to have double yolks, putting the odds against the streak at either a quintillion to one, or very considerably less, depending on whether you take into account linked odds.

This may not seem terribly important when it comes to egg yolks, but the failure to understand that some odds are linked was hugely important when it came to the financial crisis. US housing lenders had lent money to people who had a high risk of defaulting on their loans. Lots of those loans were then packaged together for investors to buy, but they were classified by ratings agencies as being low risk. How was that possible? Because the investments would pay out unless all of the mortgages in their product defaulted. Even if the risk of one borrower defaulting is relatively high, the risk of all of them defaulting is relatively low if you believe they are independent. What that ignored was the fact that the reason why one borrower might default could be linked to the reason why another defaulted, for example, a downturn in the economy or a huge housing bubble bursting.

The assumption of independent odds was also a mistake made in the tragic case of Sally Clark, who in November 1999 was convicted of the murders of her two babies and served three years in prison before being cleared. She never recovered and died in 2007 at the age of just 42. Her defence said that both babies had died of natural causes, probably sudden infant death syndrome (SIDS). One of the prosecution witnesses said that the odds of one baby dying of SIDS in Mrs Clark's household was one in 8543, and hence the chances of two babies dying of the same thing would be one in 8543 squared, which is a chance of about one in 73 million. The first mistake was to assume that the two deaths were independent. The causes of SIDS are not fully understood and you certainly cannot rule out the possibility of hereditary factors.

The Sally Clark case also raised what's called the prosecutor's fallacy, which is that because the odds against the innocent explanation are so high, the accused must be guilty. This ignores a number of problems, in particular that a mother murdering two of her babies is also extraordinarily rare. The Royal Statistical Society protested against the original judgment, pointing out that the court should not have concentrated on the odds against the innocent explanation, but weighed up the odds of the two competing explanations. Both explanations were very unlikely, but one of them had happened.

If we accept the one in 73 million figure, that's a figure trying to predict in advance whether two babies in one household are going to die of SIDS in their first year. But families were not being picked at random – Sally Clark was involved in this process because her two babies had died. So what was needed was not the odds that a random household picked from the population would suffer this tragedy, it was the odds that in a household in which this had happened, the mother would be responsible for both deaths. Given the lack of forensic evidence in the case, that certainly wouldn't have been high enough to prove her guilt beyond reasonable doubt.

Similarly, you sometimes hear claims that given the results of certain forensic tests, there is a 10 million to one chance that a particular defendant didn't commit the crime of which they are accused. Those sound like convincing odds, but only if there is some other reason to believe they did it. If they have just been picked at random, then at 10 million to one there could be six or seven other people in the UK population of 65 million who would get the same result in the tests. Of course, if the police find someone running away from the crime scene and forensic tests support the claim that they were the ones who committed the crime then it sounds like a strong case. But if the forensics lead police to arrest someone not obviously connected to the victim, that suspect could reasonably say that there is a good chance he or she didn't do it, and the judge has to be very careful in directing the jury in such cases.

So, at the end of a wide-ranging look at issues around uncertainty, risk and health stories, you now have the tools to avoid being taken in by insignificant stories. Look at whether the confidence intervals in a big survey mean that the changes in unemployment or migration that you're reading about are actually significant or are within the margin of error of the method being used to collect them. When you read scare stories about particular things causing a percentage increase in the chances of getting a particular disease, also find out what your risk of getting that disease without consuming those things would be. And when you hear about the authorities taking steps to deal with extremes, bear in mind that what goes up often comes down on its own – regression towards the mean suggests that situations will become average if they can, even without intervention. Finally, beware of the astronomical odds you sometimes see against something happening more than once – it may be that the two things are linked in ways that cut the odds.

CHAPTER 10

Economic Models

Decide whether you believe in them

On 18 April 2016 I was called into an early lock-in at the Treasury. A lock-in is what you get when something complicated is being announced at a particular time and an organisation wants to be able to explain it to journalists in advance so it can be reported correctly as soon as it's released. On this particular Monday, the Treasury was bringing out its long-awaited assessment of the cost of Brexit to the economy. We were briefed by a panel of somewhat uncomfortable-looking Treasury economists on what we could glean from the 200-page analysis in half an hour or so. The headline figure was that leaving the European Union and opting instead for a negotiated trade agreement would eventually knock £4300 per year off the UK's GDP per household. The whole lock-in was a bit of a mess because Chancellor George Osborne started his event in Bristol unveiling the analysis before the lock-in was finished, so most of the senior journalists who should have been watching it were instead locked in a windowless room in Whitehall.

The point of this chapter is not to discuss the Treasury's ability to coordinate a lock-in, but to talk about the sort of modelling that was used to come up with the £4300 a year figure.

Economies are very complicated. Economic modelling is a way of using past experience and theory to try to predict what will happen to parts of an economy in the future if particular things happen.

Getting to grips with how to dismantle an economic model is beyond the scope of this book, but there are plenty of questions you can ask without an economics degree. This chapter will cover three key questions you can ask:

- Is the conclusion justified by the model?

- Has a selection bias affected the outcome of the model?

- Are the assumptions that have gone into the model reasonable?

Is the conclusion justified by the model?

When we finally got out of the Treasury lock-in and reached a television, it turned out that Mr Osborne was in Bristol in front of a poster saying '£4,300 a year – Cost to UK families if Britain leaves the EU'. It was an interesting choice of headline figure. The conclusion of the research was that GDP (that's the value of everything produced by the UK economy) would be £120 billion a year lower in 15 years if the UK left the EU than it would have been had it stayed in. This is clearly a meaninglessly big pile of money, so the Treasury decided to divide it by something to make it more manageable. It could have done what the Leave campaign did with the EU contribution figure and divide by 52 to get a figure of about £2.3 billion a week, which would have the advantage of being easily comparable to the £350 million a week on the side of the Leave bus. Instead, the Treasury decided to divide by the number of households in the UK to get its £4300 a year. But here's the problem – a fall in GDP per household is not the same as a cost to each family. There is a relationship between the two, but it's not necessarily pound for pound because they are not the same thing. So a £4300 fall in GDP per household would cut household incomes, but not by as much as £4300.

I have since been told that the sort of model that the Treasury was running could have been used to come up with a household income figure if that was what was wanted. And indeed, the impact on household income could have been greater than £4300 per household because the falling pound would make imported goods more expensive, which hits the purchasing power of families but does not necessarily reduce GDP. But that wasn't what the Treasury did.

I published something on the BBC News website explaining the slip between GDP per household in the report and household income on the poster, which spoiled the day of Craig Oliver, Prime Minister David Cameron's director of communications, who wrote about it in his book about the campaign. I even had a phone call from a Treasury press officer trying to persuade me that GDP per household is the same thing as household income because all money eventually comes from households. But this is clearly not the case. GDP is currently about £2 trillion a year. If you divide that by the 27 million households in the UK you get about £74,000. But average household income is considerably less than that, so there is no question that these are different figures.

This wasn't a problem with the Treasury's analysis, it was a problem with what it had put on the poster. The first thing to check when you're looking at an advert, a poster or a newspaper report based on economic modelling is whether the top-line is justified by what the report actually says.

A good starting point when considering whether the claims are justified by the research is that the stronger the claim, the more likely that it's been exaggerated somewhere between the researchers and the press office. If you see a really big claim it should be sending you straight to the original research to see if there has been a slip-up between the researchers and the PR department. This happens disturbingly often because the job of promoting an institution's work may be at odds with the instincts of the people who have carried out the original research.

There was an example of this involving the *Journal of the Royal Society of Medicine* in 2017. It put out a press release saying: 'New analysis links 30,000 excess deaths in 2015 to cuts in health and social care.' Excess deaths is an estimate of the number of people who died in addition to the number who would have died anyway. If you're looking at excess deaths in winter you take a baseline of the number of people who would have died in a normal summer. Excess deaths may be due to cold weather or a particularly bad flu outbreak. The ONS brings out figures for excess winter deaths every year and there was indeed an unusually large number of excess deaths in winter 2014–15. The paper in the journal looked at some of the explanations given for the number of excess deaths and decided that they did not conclusively explain the rise. The researchers concluded in the paper that they were 'not able to reach a firm conclusion about what has happened' but added that 'the possibility that the cuts to health and social care are implicated in almost 30,000 excess deaths is one that needs further exploration'. So, the researchers had looked at why many more people had died that winter than usual, found that the reasons currently given for them were not convincing and suggested that one area worth looking into in future would be the cuts to health and social care. That translated into a press release saying that the analysis had linked the deaths with the cuts, which in February 2017 then spawned a banner headline on the front page of the *Daily Mirror*: 'Tory cuts killed 30,000'. You do not need any special qualifications in medical research to see that the conclusions of the paper did not justify the headline. Academic papers are handily structured to make them easy to check, with sections marked 'abstract' and 'conclusions' to help you understand the gist of what the research found without having to read the whole thing.

Has a selection bias affected the outcome of the model?

Selection bias sounds scary but is a fairly simple concept that you can use to impress your friends once you understand it. When you start looking out for it you will see it all over the place.

Selection bias is important in economic modelling and many other statistical areas. It is what happens when you're trying to collect data about an individual or group, but the way you are choosing is not properly random. If your economic model is based on choosing people in a way that could be skewing the results then it doesn't matter how well the rest of the model is designed, its results will be of little value. For example, I was asked to look at responses from a huge number of people who used a particular pension scheme and were answering questions about what they were going to do following a change in the rules for pension savings. The problem was that the people saving into the fund had far more pension savings than the average person in the country, so there was an immediate selection bias – all the people responding were unusually wealthy, so their responses could not tell you anything about the population as a whole. Selection bias is essentially the same as the question, raised in Chapter 1, about whether the right people are being surveyed.

Another example of selection bias was revealed in 2018 when a government minister came on Radio 4 and claimed that because people who are given community sentences are less likely to reoffend than those who are given short prison terms, community sentences should be used more. But clearly that is not a fair comparison, because judges will be more likely to give community sentences to people who they think are safer to be left in the community, which means they are considered less likely to reoffend.

Another good example was the research into weekend deaths in the NHS in 2015, to which the then Health Secretary Jeremy Hunt regularly referred when trying to get more doctors into hospitals at weekends. The study found that people admitted to hospital at the weekend were more likely to die, but warned against treating those figures as referring to avoidable deaths. It pointed out that routine operations are not carried out at weekends, so people will only be admitted to hospital then if there has been some sort of emergency. That means that those admitted at the weekend are likely to be sicker than those admitted on weekdays, which may explain the disparity.

Avoiding the effects of selection bias is important when you're trying to build an economic model based on the impact of something happening. For example, imagine you're trying to find out whether trade deals are good for an economy. Which trade deals would you look at to make that decision? If you were doing this in 20 years' time you could look at the deals done by the UK following Brexit, but the selection bias there would be that the first deals done would not be random – it would make sense to do the first deals with the countries with which the UK does the highest volume of trade. Alternatively, the first deals might be the ones that are the easiest to do or ones that maintain arrangements that are currently in place as part of the UK's membership of the European Union. In any case, it would be very difficult to identify a 'normal' deal. And the impact depends on many factors such as how far apart the countries are and how wealthy they are. All this makes building the model very difficult.

Imagine you were trying to find out what effect migrants have on jobs or wages. A way you could find out would be to look at an area that lots of migrants had moved to and see what had happened to jobs and wages there. But people do not choose places to move to at random – they will tend to go to places where there are lots of jobs and decent wages, so there is an automatic selection bias.

I talked about randomised controlled trials in Chapter 7 and they are a factor again here. If you wanted to find out the impact of migration on jobs and wages you would have to randomly choose to send one group of people to an area where there were lots of jobs available and one group to a place where there were not and see what happened. People tend not to volunteer for such research, especially if it means they might get sent to try to find employment somewhere that jobs are scarce.

An alternative is to use what are called natural experiments, for example, seeing what happens when political upheaval or conflict leads many people to move in numbers to a country for reasons other than a favourable job market. The movement of Germans from east to west following the fall of the Berlin Wall is an example of this, as is the movement of French expatriates from Algeria in the 1960s. But even these natural experiments throw up other factors, such as companies moving to the places where the migrants are arriving to take advantage of the supply of workers.

As with the question of correlation and causation in Chapter 7, the other question you need to ask yourself when considering an economic model is what else is going on here? So, for example, if you are looking at research into whether babies who are breastfed for longer tend to go on to have better outcomes in education or health, bear in mind that, at least in developed countries, mothers from higher-income backgrounds tend to breastfeed for longer and so their children already have a head start.

Selection bias crops up a lot when choosing samples for surveys, but you can see them in responses to almost anything. You probably received many emails in 2018 about the General Data Protection Regulation (GDPR) asking if organisations you don't remember ever having contacted could keep you on their databases. If you're like me, you probably replied to one or two of them straight away that you were particularly interested in and ignored the rest. If you were running the GDPR policy at an organisation, you might look at the responses you have received on the first day after sending out your email and find that 5 per cent of people had responded and three-quarters of them wanted to continue to be contacted by you. That's a perfectly reasonable statistic unless you try to do something else with it. Can you conclude that three-quarters of your current contacts want to continue to hear from you? Of course not – the responses on the first day are the people who are unrepresentatively interested in what you do. It may be that you don't have any more responses at all beyond the first day. From what I'm told by friends involved in making their organisations GDPR compliant, that that would not be unusual.

Darrell Huff in *How to Lie with Statistics* gives the example for selection bias of what would happen if you sent out a questionnaire to thousands of people asking them if they enjoyed filling out questionnaires. How many people do you think would bother returning the questionnaire to tell you that they didn't?

When you're looking at a model consider what sort of effect selection bias may have had on it. Is the effect that they are trying to model a difficult thing to measure? In particular, does it involve people making decisions? People making decisions almost always introduces selection bias, whether it's a question of if they should move to another country to work, whether they should continue to breastfeed their baby or whether they can be bothered to reply to an email.

Are the assumptions that have gone into the model reasonable?

We have a saying at Reality Check, the BBC's fact-checking team, that you can't fact-check the future.

People make predictions about things all the time – they might be right and they might be wrong. They might be right by coincidence, in ways that are in no way related to the steps the researchers took to make their predictions. Not only do we not currently know whether the predictions are right – we will almost certainly never know. Somebody making warnings about some terrible thing that will happen in the future may claim that, as a result of his warnings, action had been taken to prevent the terrible thing from happening.

The £4300 a year in the Treasury report was not a statistic – it was a forecast based on economic modelling. There are ways to check whether you think a piece of economic modelling is basically sensible, but before you do you need to take a view on whether you want to be influenced by economic modelling at all. Organisations that use it to make predictions do so because they have to in order to inform their decisions or plan their spending. They come up with their best estimates and take decisions accordingly. It's not just governments that do economic modelling. When you see an advert encouraging you to support a charity on the basis that food prices are going to double, for example, that will be a conclusion based on economic modelling.

If you are going to be influenced by it, let's start by saying that it's a tricky thing to do. The modelling carried out during the EU referendum campaign to establish what impact leaving the EU would have was particularly tricky because there were so many unknowns. We didn't know what sort of trade deals the UK would manage to do after leaving, how long they would take to negotiate, how much of the UK's contribution to the EU Budget would be saved, what that saved money would be spent on, whether the regulations that the UK government devised to replace the EU ones would be better than the EU ones and what effect all that would have on the economy. We also didn't know whether Brexit would create some sort of feel-good factor in the UK economy, or the opposite.

But what made it particularly hard was that models are built based on what particular events have done to economies in the past. We know that joining free-trade areas tends to increase trade and economic growth, but we don't know what effect leaving free-trade areas has because it hardly ever happens. Economists trying to model this looked as far back as the break-up of great empires in history to work out this effect. In the end, most of the models around the referendum were based on the idea that if joining free-trade areas was good for trade and growth then leaving them was likely to be the reverse.

The Treasury used what's called a gravity model, which considers trade between countries and models what happens to it based on factors such as how far apart they are, whether they use the same language and how rich they are. It then looks over time at what happens if some of these variables change. But you have to start out with various assumptions when you build the model, such as what happens if currencies weaken or how much signing a free-trade agreement with one country reduces the amount of trade with other countries with which you do not have an agreement. And these models are enormously sensitive to the assumptions on which they are built and the scenarios that they are supposed to be judging.

The £4300 per household figure came from the Treasury's long-term analysis, but the department also conducted short-term analysis. It suggested that a vote to leave would create an immediate and profound economic shock, push the country into recession and lead to a sharp increase in unemployment. This clearly has not happened. There are a few reasons why the predictions were wrong and the first is that David Cameron had said that following a Brexit vote he would immediately go to Brussels and trigger Article 50, which starts the process of leaving the EU. In the event this didn't happen until the end of March 2017, which was almost a year after the vote. The second problem was that it assumed that a vote to leave the EU would cause shocked consumers to reduce their spending, but missed the idea that if consumers had voted for it they probably wouldn't think it was a bad thing. Thirdly, it assumed that the government and Bank of England would not take any action to support the economy, when in fact the Bank of England cut interest rates and pumped extra money into the economy. Would you have accepted these assumptions? It was fair enough to believe that the Prime Minister would trigger Article 50 straight away. Many commentators at the time pointed out the assumption that the authorities would not take steps to support the economy. I did not see anybody point out the flaw in the assumption about consumer spending falling.

The Treasury was right in its forecast that the pound would fall sharply, but wrong in many of its other predictions of the immediate outcome. This does make me wonder whether it was a good idea for the Treasury to be involved in this sort of forecasting at all. When I asked a statistician in the civil service if he was worried that departments putting out these sorts of forecasts reduced the public's confidence in other things they publish such as official statistics, he told me that the forecasts come from the economists while the statistics come from statisticians. I'm not convinced that people recognise this distinction. The establishment of the Office for Budget Responsibility to make official forecasts for the government and keep politics out of economic forecasting was an excellent idea. Perhaps it would be a good idea if the government took advantage of this to avoid getting involved in forecasting at all. The UK's statistics regulators are trying to widen their code of conduct to include things such as economic modelling that are not actually statistics in order to prevent damage to the reputation of government departments from forecasting and other numerical releases.

This distinction between what statisticians do and what economists do is quite important although not precise – there are economists involved in the creation of official statistics just as there are statisticians who help with models and forecasting. Even so, I find it strange that almost all news organisations have economics correspondents and, as far as I know, only two have a statistics editor.

One is at the *Financial Times*. I met its head of statistics when the BBC first decided it was prepared to fund a statistics role for a trial period. I stole his title, but I did ask him first. The BBC now has a permanent head of statistics, in addition to its economics editor and correspondent, which I think has made a considerable difference to its reporting of numbers.

Should you be ignoring what economic models say? George Box, one of the greatest statisticians of the twentieth century, said: 'All models are wrong, but some are useful.' The precise numbers may be of little value, whether they are the £4300 a year figure or the Treasury's earlier declaration that every person in Scotland was £1400 a year better off inside the UK, but the direction the models predict and some of the assumptions they make are quite interesting.

My friends at the fact-checking website Full Fact

offer the analogy that you would probably listen if your doctor told you to stop eating junk food because it would make you fat, even if she couldn't tell you exactly how many kilograms you would weigh this time next year. If you buy into the assumptions then you are likely to accept the direction of travel.

As with surveys, a good first step when looking at an economic model is to look at who has conducted the research and who is paying for it. If it has been commissioned by a campaigning group you are justified in being a bit suspicious of its findings, but remember that an independent group can be just as wrong as a biased one.

Next, take a look at some of the assumptions on which the models are based. Reports in this area should be transparent about their assumptions and how the model works – if they are not you shouldn't believe them. If they are then you can take a view on whether you think they are too optimistic or too pessimistic. Also, have a look at what the report says about the level of uncertainty – the Treasury's reports were pretty good at highlighting the uncertainty in their models. Anyone claiming to know exactly how things will pan out in the future is lying to you. And remember that if you are not in a position in which you need to use economic modelling to take decisions, you could choose to ignore it altogether.

There is a middle ground here. You may take a view that the numbers you end up with as a result of an economic model are not particularly helpful, but perhaps the assumptions it uses will help you get back to first principles. The first principles for the Treasury model would be that they believe trade is a good thing because it allows the country to specialise in things that it is good at doing while importing products from other countries that are better at producing them. It could then have argued that EU membership makes trade easier with the UK's nearest neighbours and some of the world's richest economies. I wonder if going back to first principles without the numbers would have worked – people working in senior positions in both campaigns tell me they were under great pressure from the media to produce numbers and not just arguments, so perhaps not.

As long as this pressure exists it is important that you recognise what you can do to challenge the numbers being thrown at you from models. Check whether the claims are justified by the research and look at the assumptions being made. Then take a view on whether the numbers are any use to you and if you wouldn't be better going back to first principles to understand what is going on. Also, think about whether the question being asked in the modelling has introduced a selection bias – if anybody is having to take a decision then it probably has, and you need to look at how the economists have allowed for that. And if all else fails, you may be able to just ignore the models and still get on with your life.

But I really needed that figure

I'm sometimes told by colleagues that if they followed my advice then we would have nothing to report. Part of me feels that if everything available to report would have been ruled out by the ten chapters you have just read then cancelling the news and showing a selection of classic cartoons instead would be no bad thing. On 18 April 1930 in the 8.45 p.m. BBC news bulletin, the announcer declared 'There is no news' and then piano music was played for the rest of the 15-minute segment. It's hard to imagine that happening today.

But, of course, a commitment to statistical robustness does not mean abandoning all stories, it means reporting them correctly, and because you're looking back to the original research rather than just repeating what the press release says, you get a different story and generally a better one than all your competitors are running.

This is true for all uses of numbers, not just news

coverage. Most statisticians hate the quote that Mark Twain, probably incorrectly, attributed to Benjamin Disraeli, that there are three kinds of lies: lies, damned lies and statistics. Part of the reason for this is that it's hard to imagine how statistics can lie – they may be inaccurate, but I think that in order to lie you need words. Often it is not the numbers that are important: what really matters is the words around them.

This is particularly the case if you find yourself needing to use the best-available statistics, even when they are not as good as you might hope. The BBC's *Victoria Derbyshire* programme approached me to help with some research its team wanted to use about the experiences of male sex workers. Researchers had managed to get the responses of about 120 male sex workers, but this is not an easy group to survey and we believed it was the biggest sample anybody had managed to get. You know from Chapter 1 on surveys that 120 is not nearly enough to make general statements about all male sex workers, but if you choose your words carefully this is still research that can be used.

I am a great supporter of using the best research available, but only if you tell your audience what you are doing. Remember the rule of thumb that if you can explain out loud in detail where the figures have come from and what they cover without feeling foolish then they are likely to be OK. In this case, you can say that a survey of 120 sex workers found that there was considerable under-reporting of crimes against them, and hope that anyone reading it would understand that this was not an easy group to survey.

Similarly, while you now understand that costings are not an exact science, there are some areas where the best estimate is useful. If you're a politician trying to decide whether to give the go-ahead for a big infrastructure project or you are taking an investment decision at work, you are probably going to need some figures to help you decide. Evidence-based policymaking is a good thing. But just consider whether the project would be a very bad idea if the costings you have been given turn out to be drastically wrong. Give yourself a healthy margin of error around estimates of costs and benefits to come.

In that same situation, you are likely to be presented with economic models to help you take decisions. Look under the bonnet of the models and see what the estimates are based on. There's probably some useful stuff there to help with your evidence-based policymaking, even if you are dubious about the overall conclusions. Consider what the risks are if you follow the advice based on a particular model and it turns out be wrong.

When you come to tell people what decisions you have taken, always choose your language carefully to get across the uncertainty in the figures you are using. Remember that almost no government statistics are based on counting things, they are mostly estimates based on taking a sample – make sure your words reflect that. It's only when you really understand what's wrong with certain figures that you can be in a position to use the best-available figures properly. A few years ago a colleague from the BBC's Persian service asked for some advice on reporting the Iranian budget on the basis that he did not believe all of the figures in it. The answer was not to put questionable numbers in the headline or high up in the story and, most importantly, never put numbers that you are not confident about in a chart. Readers tend to believe anything in a chart passionately, however much you tell them in the text that the figures are a bit suspect. This has been my experience, and there was also some research done at Cornell University in the USA that found people were more likely to believe something if it was in a graph.

Look out for the alarm-bell words and phrases, check whether the things that correlate are really causing each other, and look out for the ways people might be trying to mislead you with averages and percentages.

Fundamentally, we do not have answers to many of these problems, but if you are aware of them then you are well ahead of the game. If you understand the flaws in some statistics then you will be able to pick the words that allow you to use the best-available data, or recognise when somebody else is failing to do so.

If you have gained one thing from reading this book, I hope it is the confidence to challenge numbers in the same way as you would challenge any other evidence. If you can do that then you will genuinely be in a position to decide whether a number, a claim or a news story is reasonably likely to be true.

Acknowledgements

I owe so much to my late father, Professor Bryan Reuben, who taught me to ask whether things are reasonably likely to be true. We had been planning to write a book together about why costing is bogus when he died. I am also indebted to my mother, who has taught me so much, and in whose house I wrote this book. My wife Susan has given love, support and suggestions throughout the process, not to mention actually reading the book and making useful comments. My children Isaac, Emily and Boaz have taught me that I always need to concentrate when answering questions.

My agent Ben Clark from LAW has been extremely enthusiastic about the project from the start and coaxed me through the process with great skill and understanding. As soon as I met my editor Claire Chesser from Constable I knew that I wanted to work with her – she's great. Howard Watson copy-edited the book and is the first person who has ever suggested that I use too many adjectives. I was delighted.

I have been promoting statistical robustness at the BBC for at least a decade with the help of many very special people, especially Jonathan Baker, who managed to find funding for me to spend 18 months as the corporation's first head of statistics. That mantle has now been taken on by Robert Cuffe who has proper statistical qualifications and is learning to be a journalist with alarming speed.

Building the Reality Check brand has been enormous fun and would not have happened without Jonathan Paterson, Alexis Condon, Tamara Kovacevic, Rachel Schraer, Peter Barnes, Tom Edgington, Juliette Dwyer, Liz Corbin, Rupert Carey, Chris Morris and a whole range of scarily knowledgeable researchers. Thanks to my friends at the Office for National Statistics, especially those in the press office who have made me the most spoiled journalist in the country. Also Glen Watson, the now retired director general of the ONS, who was a huge support in my early work as head of statistics and lent me first Jamie Jenkins and then Steph Howarth to help. I'm also grateful to everyone at the Royal Statistical Society, which has been very supportive throughout.

Thanks to Marc Webber for the joke about making up the numbers, to Richard Posner for pointing me towards the reporting of crime statistics in Nottingham and to Jen Clarke for finding all the double yolks. Daniel Vulkan, Sarah Lowther and Nick Blain also pointed me towards examples I could use.

Several people have generously agreed to read drafts of all or part of this book and made helpful suggestions. The first to read it were my brother David, who is the most numerically pedantic person I know, and Adi Bloom, who is the most grammatically pedantic. Corinne and Ben Sheriff, David Cowling, David Sumpter, Robert Cuffe and Malcolm Balen also gave me the benefit of their expertise and made useful suggestions.

Any errors are of course my fault – I look forward to an eagle-eyed reader finding one.